Praise for Studie

Spencer's observations about writing are always intelligent and well-reasoned . . . But you won't understand the great wisdom in Spencer's process until you've read his fiction. Story after story, these are—well, I almost said "jewels," but jewels are hard, impenetrable, and only valuable as decoration. Spencer gets to the heart of each character . . . Spencer does include one of my favorite science fiction stories in at least a decade [*What I Done*] . . . If I were a member of SFWA I would nominate it for a Nebula . . . His contemporary stories take you into every social stratum, giving you experiences I hope you haven't had, and illuminating, with every tale, what goes on inside all those mysterious unknowable human beings you live among.

Orson Scott Card, *New York Times* bestselling author of *Ender's Game*

More books on writing should be like this: story, inspiration and analysis, plus invaluable essays on writing. A feast for writers of all levels. Even non-writers will enjoy the stories and their sources of inspiration. Highly recommended!

Rick Taubold, editor-in-chief *Fabula Argentea* magazine and author of *Punctuation for Fiction Writers*

"Thirteen magnificent little gems, complete with commentaries . . . both entertaining and informative…"

Barbara Scott Emmett, award-winning author of *Dog Leap Stairs*

"A stunning collection of stories. What shines is the artful command of voice, as natural as breathing and essential to the semblance of life. The essays reveal both the person of the writer and the process of writing and how the two are serendipitously and necessarily linked. The effect is like getting bonus features on a DVD. This should be a classic primer."

Frank Ladd, author of *Gein*

"Anyone with an itch to write might well use *Studies in Fiction* as a textbook. First vs. third, foreshadowing, voice, suspense—I suspect this work will find its way into more than one college-level syllabus."

DeForest Day, author of the *Bugle Boy Cozy Mystery Series*

"Spencer writes with authority and precision on the craft of writing and includes insights into his own creative process. Whether you're starting out, an experienced author, or simply like a damn good read, there's something for everyone. Did I mention that he creates fascinating characters and beautiful prose?"

Shirley Golden, prize-winning author of *Exposing the False Moon*

STUDIES IN FICTION

13 Stories, Annotations on Each Story, and
14 Essays on Writing

WILLIAM L SPENCER

The purpose of this book: Though these ebook and paperback editions carry a
price and therefore appear to be commercial in nature, it has been understood
from the beginning that there is little, if any, likelihood that they will ever generate
revenues commensurate with the tens of years and the tens of thousands of hours
required for their creation and production. This being the case, the prime impetus
for persevering in publication is to make available to students and readers in
public, academic, and andragogy fields important scholarship, research, and
education in the areas of aesthetics, linguistics, and taxonomy.

E-Book ISBN 978-0-9776263-3-5
Paperback ISBN 978-0-9776263-4-2
Library of Congress Control Number: 2022907665

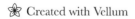 Created with Vellum

For convenience, the stories are numbered; the commentary on each story and the essays are not. Each story is followed by an annotation describing how the story came about.

The essays are things I've come across, experienced, and considered through the years involving the writing of fiction.

You'll find additional information on the blog:

www.StudiesInFiction.net

Contents

Every mind contains multitudes

Christopher Wylie

An Actor Prepares

Stanislavski had his ideas. Here's another.

THE PARTY WAS ALL SMOKE AND NOISE, seventy people, maybe ninety, mostly high, jammed into the second floor of an old clapboard house at the beach. Two big speakers hammered out bone-cracking throbs, a screaming rapper. Conversations bellowed, joints passed, a bewildering, deafening blur.

Nikki, her butt against a buffet, as far away from the speakers as she could get, a glass of wine in one hand a cigarette in the other, scanned the room. There was a time when it would have been fun, a party like this. But they were all so young and, Jesus, she was only twenty-seven.

There was that, and then there was the darkness, as if a shroud had settled about her.

She eased away from the guy who'd been trying to talk to her. Not Benjamin. Benjamin was over on the other side of the room yelling in the ear of a dorky kid in rimless glasses who had invented some kind of app that was either big or was going to be big or was something else, she didn't know and didn't care.

The guy trying to talk to her was okay and actually about as out-of-place as she was, older if maybe thirty was older, clean-cut, tweed jacket, no tie. He looked like a professor at a girl's school. She couldn't hear a word he was saying. She'd had it with this party.

"Gotta go!" she yelled, "Nice talking to you!" turning away, not caring if he heard or understood. Jesus, what a zoo.

Hands occupied with the wine and cigarette, she used her elbow to push open the sagging screen door and made her way down dilapidated wooden stairs. Wary of her silk dress, the flaking paint, she stepped gingerly in heels, watching for cracks between the boards. Following a narrow alley, she emerged onto the wide sidewalk that separated the buildings from the beach.

And there it was, the Pacific Ocean.

The sun had dipped below the horizon, a swath of neon pink and fuchsia splashed across the sky. It looked like a set decorator's idea of a sunset, a wash of vibrant pastels on a pale blue scrim. Way over the top.

Nikki crossed the sidewalk, took the big step down onto the sand and after half-a-dozen clumsy strides, stopped and looked around to make sure no one was watching. A scattering of pedestrians strolled the oceanfront walk, some kids cruised on rollerblades, but... what the hell. She dropped the wine glass where she stood. Littering a California beach, a major felony, probably punishable by death.

> I'm a naughty girl,
> No need to sham
> You know I am.

It came to her in theatre speech, that fake British accent everyone had to learn in drama school, so it must have been something she'd heard or even sung, but she couldn't remember where.

Standing on one foot then the other, she pulled off her shoes. The sand would raise hell with her pedicure, but Benjamin wouldn't be looking at her toenails.

Holding the shoes by the straps, she trudged down to where the beach slipped wet and compacted into the ocean, the waves dissolving in a foamy wash that rolled over her feet.

She turned and looked back, wondering if Benjamin would notice she was gone. The house, half-hidden behind a row of newer, nicer places, was a faded, sun-bleached green. The skinny kid Benjamin was shouting at wanted everyone to know he paid a million-five for it, all cash, three day close, and it was a teardown. As if a million-five was a big deal a hundred feet from the beach.

She listened for the music but it didn't carry. No reach, no substance, no... what? Not worth thinking about. What difference did it make? None.

She tried to track down what did matter: her desire, her ambition. It wasn't there. For the first time since she'd come to L.A., since way before L.A., it wasn't there. MIA. It was unnerving not to have that steady sense of it urging her. It was the thing that kept her going. What had Vanick called it in Performance Practicum? The little engine in your gut that keeps saying you know you can.

The stupid little engine was off the rails.

All that was left were things she didn't want: she didn't want to be at this party, she didn't want to smoke a couple joints, she didn't want to go home with Benjamin. Especially that. She knew if she did she'd end up letting him do it to her. Even if she didn't feel like it, he'd be endlessly yapping at her, and she knew eventually she'd give in just to get him to shut up. Then she'd end up with the shitty feeling of having done something she didn't want to. What had Vanick called it? Going against one's nature, a disenchantment.

But fuck it, what was the diff? Everywhere she found herself was somewhere she didn't want to be.

The only thing she wanted was to be away from it all. Particularly, right now.

Benjamin.

Sooner or later he'd remember and ask her if she got the part. Telling him had been a huge mistake. When she'd gotten home that night, showered, scrubbed herself, washed her hair, wrapped herself in her fluffy robe, still buzzed from the drinks and the wine, she had to talk to someone. So she called him and told him about the movie, she was sure she had the part.

She took a final drag on her cigarette and flipped it at the waves, realizing she'd left her clutch bag with the Parliaments and her Dunhill lighter on the buffet. She couldn't lose the lighter. Michael Brockton had given it to her two years ago when he'd taken her to the Oscars—he'd been one of the stars in a nominated picture and her character—Sexy Cocktail Waitress—had two lines. Her wardrobe was four-inch heels, black net stockings, a tiny skirt and fitted top. He'd flirted with her on the set. It didn't matter that she hadn't seen him since. It was a souvenir from the Oscars, a Dunhill Pinstripe Palladium Rollagas, a goddamned five-hundred dollar lighter.

Shit.

She plodded back across the sand. When she reached the step from the beach up to the sidewalk, she decided to hell with the dress and sat down on the concrete, brushed at her feet. She couldn't get the grit out from between her toes. To hell with that too. She didn't want to put on her shoes anyway, and she didn't want to go back inside. She didn't want to do anything.

But she was hungry, she needed a cigarette. She sat there, her shoes in her lap, and watched the night fold out over the Pacific, remembering Michael Brockton and the Oscars and how the trades always mentioned his captivating crooked smile, weighing what she would have to do to get the lighter against how much she didn't want to put up with Benjamin.

Maybe it was the ocean, the sky, the sunset, the inexorable

gathering of day into night, this perfect seascape evening sliding down the western slope of the world. Maybe it was a moment of lonely calm. From wherever it came, the awareness floated into her mind that she had enough pills in her medicine cabinet. If she didn't want to, she would never again have to put up with anything. Never again, not ever.

It was appealing, the possibility of floating away into nothingness, letting go of the endless pretending, never having to look at her face in a mirror. But it was frightening: an icy feeling that curled around her stomach.

It was fall-out.

Tuesday of last week she'd come out of the hotel room, the Ritz-Carlton Laguna Beach, the heavy door swinging closed behind her, the lock clicking into place with a steel-embedded-in-oak finality. It was like the last sound that echoes through a theatre at the end of a good noir picture. The audience is hushed, then the sound of that clicking lock breaks the tension and everyone can let out the breath they didn't know they'd been holding.

The door closed behind her and Nikki walked down the hallway—luxurious carpet, cream walls, tasteful paintings—buoyed by how he'd been afterward, how he'd smoothed things over, how affable and charming he became. But no hint of an apology. Yeah, that was a producer's skill, sticking it to the talent and then making believe everything was fine and dandy, and even, really, all for the best. Hey, what was the harm? Just something between friends.

She'd been tipsy, well actually pretty piddly-eyed, but she knew what was happening every moment, saw it with the clarity that comes with enough champagne cocktails. You might not be able to drive too well—though actually she had driven herself home, no problem—but you could see the face and the eyes of the person you were with, see what was behind them.

He was the executive producer—he was always the executive

producer on all his projects—and she could tell he wanted her for the picture, he'd made up his mind. Ensconced in that wonderful cocktail lounge, damask silk sofas that looked like French antiques, twenty-foot windows at the top of a hundred-foot cliff above an endless ocean, they'd had a wonderful conversation. He was completely delightful, and he knew everyone. His stories were so observant and droll, inside anecdotes that made her laugh, included her among his closest friends. He was a raconteur, the magazine stories said that about him, and it was completely true. After a couple hours, she didn't know how many drinks, he said he needed to give her the script, it was in his room.

He led her to the bed, his hand on her elbow, told her to sit. He stood in front of her, took her hand and put it on his boner. Told her to take it out.

And there she was. Jesus. Not a friend, not a colleague. He wasn't the worldly, virtuous man he seemed to be, above and beyond this kind of tawdry bullshit.

Just another arrogant asshole with a boner.

She knew better than to get herself into this situation. She despised that it turned out to be this, so trashy, so crude, hated herself for being so stupid, letting down her guard, wanting to believe he was different, allowing herself to be lulled into this, sitting on the bed, her hand on the front of his pants.

She knew she had a choice—it was clear in her mind, she wasn't some dumb kid, she'd been around the block—she pictured herself standing up, heading for the door, throwing a fuck you over her shoulder, even pausing with the door open, calling him a scuzzy piece of shit. But she couldn't bring herself to stand. The situation held her frozen: who he was... who he was... what the picture was going to be, her face on the poster, he'd told her that—her face would be on the poster—he'd said it twice, and how could she not believe it? She could imagine the poster. If she walked out, told him fuck you, then she would be marked as an ungrateful little cunt, uncooperative, difficult to work with, maybe worse. Word would go out.

It's only because I'm drunk, it came to her as she slid his zipper down. I'm drunk and he'll like me.

And then her only thought was get it over with. He was saying something, his hands buried in her hair, but her mind was walled off, a metronome, get it over with, get it over with.

She could tell when he was about to finish and tried to pull away, but he held her tight.

When he finally released her, she ran into the bathroom, spit in the sink and used the Listerine until the little bottle was empty. She sat on the toilet lid and told herself to calm down, to stop thinking about it.

After ten minutes she went out, legs wooden, ashamed, afraid to look at him, the derision and condescension she might see in his face. She grabbed her purse and went back in the bathroom, washed her face where she'd cried, fixed her lipstick, reapplied her mascara, brushed her hair. She wanted to never leave the bathroom, but she couldn't put it off forever.

He was waiting, trousers fastened, shirt tucked in, hair smoothed, an amazing warm smile on his face. He took her hand, he was sweet, so kind, she had to admit. He'd opened the drapes in front of the window wall that looked out over the lighted swimming pool and tennis courts. He led her to a chaise and seated her as if she were royalty. He poured chardonnay from a bottle in a silver bucket, all iced and ready—yeah, he was a producer, all right—and handed her a beautiful fluted glass. Baccarat. He was so easy and gracious that by the time they'd finished the chardonnay and she walked out of the room, her head whirling, she felt like she'd come through it all unscathed. Well, almost.

The next day she called the studio, the number he'd written on the cover of the script. When she gave her name, the secretary took a minute to find a list then said, uninterested: "Oh, yeah, sorry, casting is complete."

The bastard.

She was such a dunce. She'd been so weak, so afraid the asshole wouldn't like her.

She spent the rest of the day at the gym, sweating like a stevedore, trying to find her way into a shell where nothing could reach her.

Sitting on the sidewalk, looking at the ocean, she considered what a fucking predator he was. How often had he done the same thing to other girls? Her humiliation was like a tide that carried everything before it. She'd flinched. She'd betrayed herself, breached something inside she hadn't really understood was there. An iron hollowness had coalesced in the pit of her stomach.

She shivered. It was darker.

Her clutch bag floated in front of her, and for a second she thought she was hallucinating, or a UFO had materialized in the sky. Then she heard his voice, realized who it was.

"You left your purse."

The clean-cut guy from the party, his shoes crunching on the sandy sidewalk.

She took the bag as he sat beside her.

"You're a lifesaver." She took out the Parliaments, fished for the lighter. "I was dying for a cigarette, but I couldn't stand the thought of going back in. I was sitting here feeling sorry for myself."

Was that what she'd been doing? Was that all it was, feeling sorry for herself?

"My name's Kenneth. Ken." He reached over and took the lighter, not letting her hand go, keeping it cupped with both his as he snapped a flame. It was a moment: she pictured how it would look on-camera—his strong, warm hands holding hers, the glow of the flame on her face.

She blew a stream of smoke out of the side of her mouth, examined him. "That was very smooth, very Cary Grant." He had a nice, open face and broad shoulders beneath his tweed jacket.

"I surprised myself. I'm not that cool, I mean, I don't even smoke. But..." He paused a second. "Can I tell you something?" he went on, not waiting for an answer, "I wanted to touch your hand, you're so pretty—"

She put two fingers to his lips, stopped him. He had a good jaw. She liked that too. And he had confidence.

"So Kenneth," she said, pulling back a bit, "you teach algebra at Marymount?"

"Hardly. I'm a resident at UCLA Medical Center."

"A doctor?"

He nodded.

"What are you doing here?"

"Jeremy, the guy who's throwing the party, I examined him this morning and he invited me. Actually he invited everyone on the floor but I'm the only one who showed up."

"He was seeing a doctor? What's wrong with him?"

"You want me to breach patient confidentiality?" He gave her a smile that seemed to say maybe I'm serious and maybe I'm not.

"You have to." The cigarette made an orange streak as she waved it in front of his face. She tried for a flat tone like Obi-Wan: "You will tell the girl everything."

He held her eyes for a few seconds, she watched him decide, then, "He's losing his hearing."

They stared at each other, then both of them broke into laughter.

Her mood lifted, the doom and gloom were dissipating. A Cary Grant kind of guy, a doctor no less, the night coming down around them, she could play this—the vault of sky an immense proscenium arch.

But it wasn't a play, it had to be a movie, the crew scattered across the sand, the video village over there, big Softbox lights on stands, track laid, the craft truck somewhere on a nearby street, PAs on either end of the sidewalk holding back the rollerbladers.

She could almost hear Vanick's voice from the classroom, that quiet way he had of starting a scene the same way Stanislavsky had done it: "*Begin.*"

"Listen," her tone became serious, "I have to tell you something."

"You can tell me anything."

He was so open, his line so perfectly sincere. For a moment Nikki had an urge to confess, tell him the whole pathetic episode. Then she caught herself. She could never tell anyone.

"You followed me out here."

"You forgot your purse."

He was wonderful. His presence changed the quality of the darkness. Was it him or would anyone do? No, it needed to be the right sort of someone with a nice jaw, sincere brown eyes, and a tweed jacket. It looked like Harris Tweed.

She flipped her cigarette away, reached up to press her palm against his cheek, his beard bristly. She watched his confusion.

Men were so silly. When you touched them unexpectedly they got all flummoxed. He could be Cary Grant and she was Eva Marie Saint and it was *North by Northwest* if Hitchcock had shot it on the beach in Venice. She lowered her voice, picked up the deepening shadows: "It's enough that we've found each other." She watched him. It was right there in his face. He'd never met anyone like her.

Yes, this was real. This was who she really was. He would love her, and all the others out there on the other side of the camera lens, everyone in the world, all of them would love her too.

"Darling?" she let him know he'd missed his cue.

"Yes." He stammered, making it a half question.

"Listen, darling," she let fear come across her eyes, expanding the moment. It was such fun, she knew how good she was, showing the dread of Benjamin as played by the cruel James Mason.

She reached down and took his hand, pulling it up against her so that he would know how desperately she needed him. She turned—only her head, making sure she would stay in-frame because at this point it would be a tight shot only on her—and looked down the alleyway toward the green house.

"They're back there, at the party, planning the whole thing out." It was such a plot hole, as if anyone could make any plans in all that noise. But they'd fix it in post. She turned back to him, medium tempo. There would be a cut here to a two-shot favoring him, she would be in profile.

And he wasn't bad, considering. He had a hopeful look, not knowing what the hell was going on, but wanting to be part of it —hell, wanting to be part of anything so long as she was there.

"I've got to get away from here, darling," speaking quickly, the impending danger, Benjamin coming to look for her. "It's all too complicated, I can't explain." How often had she heard that line in a movie—skipping over all the stuff the audience already knew, moving the story along.

A tilt of her head, not too much, as she let her shoulders fall. She knew how vulnerable she looked, how well she was selling it. "You've got to trust me." She looked up into his eyes. "Somehow, for some crazy reason, destiny has brought us together and you're the only one who can save me."

He was smiling, not understanding but up for anything. "Whatever you say."

It wasn't exactly great.

"We have to run, darling, we have to run to the ends of the earth." Even as she said it, so melodramatic, wondering where it came from, she realized how true it was, how she wanted to slip over the horizon with the sun, disappear to the other side of the world. She was through with Benjamin. She would close the door on Benjamin, banish it all.

"To the ends of the earth." He butchered it, but it didn't matter, he was wonderful!

"Oh, darling!" she let her eyes melt into his. She loved calling him darling, she could see the effect it had on him. "We have to hurry!"

He scrambled to his feet, took her purse and shoes, helped her up.

"My car's down there," he pointed.

As they started down the sidewalk she wrapped both arms around one of his, sheltering herself against him, feeling the tweed against her cheek. He would love her, this good, strong man. He would fall madly, hopelessly, in love with her. He was halfway there already.

She looked out at the western sky where night had fallen. Yes, it was time to move on, forget the past.

She pressed his arm, feeling it against her. She would have such fun with him. He might be the one. She imagined the two of them together, playing house forever and ever, a lovely haze of infatuation and pretending. Yet even as she thought it she knew it wouldn't last—after all it never did—and then she felt a whisper of guilt, the merest brush, easily ignored, that came with the sneaking uneasiness that she would probably break his heart.

And that other? She'd try to forget it, though she knew she would only be trying, that she'd never be rid of it, not entirely. It would be down there somewhere, sealed away, deep in the darkness, where she could reach out to it if she ever needed to, if a certain sort of role ever came along.

Using Inner Monologue to
Write "Actor"

The story was conscious all the way, nothing inspired no divine intervention of the muse, so for those of you who find the story interesting and might be curious, here's how it came about.

I started with the idea of writing a little exercise using a technique I'd just discovered: the inner monologue, or inner dialogue or internalization, it's called different things.

Steve Day (pen name Deforest Day) put me onto this: In her blog *This Itch of Writing*, which is well worth a visit, Emma Darwin, PhD, points out that this technique is correctly called Free Indirect Discourse, a translation from the French *discours indirect libre*.

In her blog, Dr. Darwin gives this example of how it works:

> *Emily was one of those people who hated confronting liars. She put down her coffee and thought, he's a bastard! He's obviously lying! She picked up her coffee again. "How sweet of you to be so honest."*

[F]ree indirect style integrates thoughts and speech into the narrative:

> *Emily was one of those people who hated confronting liars. She*

put down her coffee. He was a bastard! He was obviously lying. She picked up her coffee again and said how sweet it was of John to be so honest.

At the time I started the story, I was following my idle curiosity the way I do, and I'd read a Daphne du Maurier novel in which internal monologue, or *free indirect discourse*, was almost the whole book. One of the things I found so fascinating about how du Maurier did it, and the technique I learned from her that I imitated altogether when I wrote this story, thinking it was a good idea, is to simply have the main character say, through the internal monologue, what the story problem is. Why mess around, try and be subtle, go through contortions trying to work it in? Just have her come out and say it. After all, it's something the reader wants to know.

Go ahead, read *Frenchman's Creek* for yourself, the part starting in Chapter 2, the tenth paragraph down, that begins, "Dona stared moodily out of the window..." You don't have to buy the book to read this part, though the book is a good read, just use the Look Inside feature on Amazon.

Now, I think this is important: the lovely part of the technique is that it lodges the story question right in the reader's mind, directly from the character to the reader; "here's how it is for me," the character says, and that's it.

The phrase "story question" might bother you. That kind of nomenclature once bothered me too. It sounds cold and manipulative, artificial, and far from what I want my stories to be. I certainly don't want my reader to feel like she's being jerked around like a puppet or pushed this way or that. But it doesn't bother me anymore; now it feels comfortable. What's more, now I know in an empirical two-plus-two way what's going on when I get to the story question, and I think I'm in a better position to mess with it and get it to do the job that needs doing. It's easier and surer to have a bit of empirical knowledge, to think "this is the way they say it needs to work" rather than to rely entirely on your intuition.

Story question is a little misleading, though. The writer doesn't actually *ask* a question. What she does is have the character make a statement or think a thought, and this thought lodges the question in the reader's mind to be concerned about. For Nikki, it happens when she thinks:

> *From wherever it came, the awareness floated into her mind that she had enough pills in her medicine cabinet. If she didn't want to, she would never again have to put up with anything. Never again, not ever.*

I added a couple sentences to try and strengthen the implication that if she continued to feel this way, she might very well kill herself. That's what I wanted the reader worried about, that's the over-riding issue of dramatic tension. So at this point, hopefully I've got the reader rooting for this girl, hoping she pulls out of her emotional nosedive, and wondering what caused it.

I think one of the key things about putting the story question into internal monologue is that it is totally bound up with how the character feels about herself. However the character feels, that's how the reader is going to understand her feeling, and even if the reader doesn't consciously catch on to other stuff, she still receives the force of the implication. It sounds so simplistic and obvious to describe it that way, but when you're in the throes of composition, dealing with it (or trying to) in dramatic terms, and you haven't got the damn story written yet, it can seem a lot more difficult.

The implication.

That's what so much of fiction writing is about: putting the implication into the readers sub-mind, that level just a shade below conscious here-and-now.

Is there such a thing, am I making all this up?

Ever pass someone on the street (it happens when you're walking in Manhattan), catch their eyes and get a creepy feeling, know somehow that things are not right with them, know this without really stopping to consider it? What you saw in that person's eyes went into what I call your sub-mind. The person coming along behind you, with a little more access to their sub-mind, or perhaps with less to worry about, or who at the moment is less distracted, might think, "That guy is a raging psychopath." That's how I think the sub-mind works, and that's where I think a lot of fiction creates its effect. (I read an article in the *New Yorker* that talked about mirror neurons in the brain and it seems to me that's the mechanism that makes fiction work. Same thing, more scientific. (The book *The Tell-Tale Brain* by V.S. Ramachandran, M.D. has an interesting discussion of mirror neurons.)

Once I decided to try and write a story using the technique, I scrolled down my hard drive looking for a starting point, and came across a fragment that I'd written maybe thirty years ago, when I was living in a studio apartment on High Tower Drive, behind the Hollywood Bowl. It was something I'd never used.

The sun was almost down, a swath of neon pink sunset splashed across the western horizon. The tide had turned and the waves were small, little more than a gentle wash that rolled softly up the beach then expired with a sigh.

As she watched, the street lights came on and were reflected from the wet sand where the waves receded. Someone had a window open, their stereo turned up. The cadences of a Mozart concerto floated out upon the evening air, seeming to settle all about her, like a benediction.

That girl on the beach was the starting point, but the paragraph never made it into the story. After I'd written the story, but before it was published, a publication called *Pure Slush* said they were looking for beautiful short pieces. I submitted the two paragraphs above and they were accepted, so that item is in *The Beautifullest, Pure Slush* Vol. 17, on Amazon last time I looked.

In my mind, the girl on the beach was an actress, of course. Who else would she be?

My sophomore year at the University of Washington, I started hanging out with the drama majors. Some of the guys were older, vets coming back to school on the G.I. Bill, and many of the girls were pretty. The drama majors often talked about a professor named Vanick Galston. I never met him or talked to him, and according to the internet he has passed on, but the name Vanick seemed to me to be just right, so I used it in the story for Nikki's drama professor.

After graduating, two years in the Army, and a year or so in Seattle as a clerk in the freight department of what was then the Northern Pacific Railroad, I bought an old 4-door Dodge for a couple hundred bucks and headed for Los Angeles, where one of my drama school pals, James T. Callahan, was working as an actor. What ended up in the story was a lot of what I absorbed during this Hollywood period.

The opening of the story was one I hit on right away, the party in the old house near the beach. I knew she was an actress right from the beginning, so of course the immediate problem she feels is one of getting old, things passing her by. Many years ago my niece, Diane Hume, took my wife and I to a party in San Francisco's Haight District, and it was like that, an apartment jammed with people, loud music, everyone high and getting higher. So that was easy to portray and a natural starting point: Something underway of possible interest to the reader, an unhappy protagonist. From there, it was a matter of following my nose and letting things specific to who the character was becoming in my mind and on the page continue to reveal themselves. I can't tell you how or why that happens, and I've discussed it with several other writers. It just does happen. But I've got a theory, and it's this: There isn't any dividing line between the conscious and unconscious mind. Rather, the mind is like the ocean, a gradient from surface light to the deepest dark memories and associations floating around way down there somewhere. When you get into the creative flow, you open things up, stand to the side in the Zen sense, allow stuff that's down there to bubble up. And the more you do it, the more that process seems to occur. The more you try to be creative, the more you ask your unconscious writing mind to produce, the more responsive your writing mind becomes. So you're going along, tapping the keyboard, and the tune floats into your mind: *I'm a naughty girl, no need to sham, you know I am…* and there it is, a bubble popping up from God knows where. I have no idea where or when I'd ever heard that before, but it must have been at some dramatic production at the university.

But now I have to spoil the story for you, probably spoil it forever. When I got Nikki out to the beach with the wavelets washing over her feet, I had to get her back to the party or at least to the sidewalk. So I made up the stuff about the expensive cigarette lighter (I found the lighter on the internet), and to justify that, I made up the stuff about the imaginary character Michael Brockton, and the cheesy movie magazine quotes and going to the Oscars. That rationale didn't bubble up from my unconscious, it isn't an organic part of the story, it's stuff I manufactured right on the surface. When I wrote it, I felt a prickling on my skin, and thought, "Oh, this is so phony, no one is ever going to go for this." But I left it in, and not a single person who ever read the story for me, and there were, over the years, probably a couple dozen sets of eyes on it, ever said anything about that part. I guess it does work for who Nikki is, that part of her that goes for the phony bullshit, but it still gives me a twinge.

I wrote that above paragraph, and only now, some days later, do I realize how crazy it sounds. What I'm claiming is that Nikki, a product of my imagination, occupies among my neurons some certain territory that is authentically her, and yet there is another part of my imagination outside of the authentic Nikki that I chose to exercise, thereby imposing on the authentic Nikki some bogus stuff just to make the story work.

Perhaps this seemingly strange state of affairs isn't so remarkable when you realize what it is we're working with. According to V. S. Ramachandran, M.D., The human brain has about 100 billion neurons, and each neuron makes from a thousand to ten thousand contacts with other neurons. So the number of possible brain states is staggeringly vast, and easily exceeds the number of elementary particles in the known universe. And one thing about myself that I know for sure is that in almost all biological, physiological, and psychological respects, I am distressingly normal. If my brain can be this way, have a partition which I identify as authentically Nikki, then anyone's brain can do it.

Thinking about this takes me back to my first piece of what might be called fiction. When I was in the sixth grade, maybe ten or eleven, I'd talked my mother into buying me a Kodak Brownie camera. I think they cost a dollar. I went through a period of taking a roll of the 120 film every few weeks. One winter's day in Madison, Wisconsin, where we lived on Rutledge Street, just across from Lake Monona, just down the block from Orton Park, I took a little plastic airplane I had, just a small one, wingspan maybe two or three inches, and put it on a snowbank that had been shoveled up from the sidewalk in front of the apartment house where we lived. I stood above the airplane, and took a picture of it, the dark outline of the airplane among the heaps of snow. When I got the prints back from the drugstore on the corner of Williamson Street, I took the picture of the tiny plane in the snow to Marquette Elementary school and showed it to my classmates, telling them it was a picture of a crashed plane in the mountains that I'd taken from the window of a flight to visit my father in Spokane. Everyone believed me. Or at least no one called me on it to my face. By that time I was an apt liar, perhaps even a skilled liar, but that was the first time I manufactured something and passed it off as real, my first step into fiction. I learned that if I made it seem real, I could get them to go for it.

The oldest draft of this story on my hard drive dates from November 2008, and is the fourth draft of what I was calling *Naughty Girl*. Then in 2017 the title changed to *This Hollywood Life* and it's about 600 words shorter. From the beginning, my idea was to start Nikki at the party and then take her out to the beach. Once I got the story question in, I had an idea of where I wanted to get to. In the back of my mind was the core of what takes place at the Ritz Carlton, but I had only a vague idea in mind for the actual events. I was thinking that's where I wanted to go, but I wasn't sure I'd be able to get there, or if I did get there, I had no idea how in the world I'd write it.

I felt stuck. What do I do now? I knew I wanted to get to the Ritz Carlton scene and I had an idea of the general shape it would take (they have drinks, they go up to his room, etc.). But I didn't want to start the scene with they meet, they order drinks, they sit down, they chit-chat, blah blah blah. It was all a vague blur, a lot of non-dramatic folderol that isn't going to be very interesting. The producer and the actress, it's all stereotyped and clichéd.

I had just suggested to an online writing friend that he cut out a bunch of stuff from his story and start the scene as deeply into it as possible. That thought came to me: why not start the scene way deep into it? Hell, I said to myself, I'll just start this scene as deeply into it as humanly possible! So I started it with the only clear image I had in my mind: The hotel room door closing behind her as she leaves the room and the scene is over. I thought it was sort of amusing in a cryptic, writerly way, to start a scene deep in with the last thing that happens when the scene ends. You can't start any further in than that, I said to myself. What I wanted to get in was the sound of that door closing, a very expensive door and a very expensive lock. Then, being in Nikki's mind, and she is in a heightened state, she characterizes the sound in a context that's part of her life. I think readers like it because it's vivid and sounds so plausible. Re-reading it, it feels to me like a special moment that gives the reader impetus, propels him forward into the story.

It seemed to work. As soon as the door closed behind her, since I was in internal monologue, I had to write her reaction to the scene she'd just been involved in (though I didn't know at that point in any detail what had happened in the scene because I hadn't worked it out or written it yet). But I knew she wasn't going to feel good during the scene itself, so I went for the opposite: I made her feel a sense of half-assed achievement after the hotel room door closes.

And it makes logical sense on a feeling level. What do you say when you leave the dentist's office after having a tooth pulled? You say, hell, that wasn't so bad. You say that because the anticipation of having a tooth pulled is often worse than actually going through it with a hefty dose of Novocain, and afterwards you say it wasn't so bad because you got it over with and probably the Novocain hasn't worn off yet.

At this point I should mention that my first inclination in writing something is a tendency to do the opposite. The opposite of where the characters are, the opposite of what the reader expects. So if the character is happy at the beginning (Oedipus is crowned king) he will be unhappy at the end (he finds out he's been sleeping with his mom and gets his eyes poked out). Why do the opposite? It makes it interesting. Cast against type: make the heroine morally challenged. It's more fun that way. I don't know what you need for a reason, but that does it for me.

Once I got the door closed and her reacting, the rest was straight-forward: Her internal monologue giving an overview of what happened, all from her tight personal point of view. It's easy because she gets to characterize things and to give the highlights. It's an announcer's play-by-play. All the clerk typist has to do is watch the pace, stay just ahead of the reader, and pay attention to sentence variety.

It does contain my most favorite line from the story:

She grabbed her purse and went back in the bathroom, washed her face where she'd cried,

That's it, no embellishment necessary.

The next scene transition, from the phone call and the reaction back to sitting there at the beach thinking about how she doesn't like herself anymore, was straight-forward. You can take your character as far away as you want, in space or time, and when you bring her back, all you have to do is have her feel the same as she felt before, and you're home free. Once again, it's nice to know there's a technique for this and you don't have to figure anything out; follow the dotted lines. (This technique is straight out of Dwight Swain's book, *Techniques of the Selling Writer.*)

The dialogue between Nikki and the guy from the party was fun to write. I love that stuff; I wish I'd been writing movies back in the 30s and 40s, I would have loved it, I'm such a romantic fool.

The really good thing about having the clean-cut guy show up when he does is that it is a surprise to the reader when it happens, and then it clicks in as inevitable. Granted, it's not a big surprise; it's just a small one. It also helps keep the story tight; the character is already there in the beginning, so it's "oh, yeah, of course, he likes her, she left her purse..."

The tone of the story changes so much from where her feelings are at and then to her transition into being an actress that I did revision after revision, never being quite satisfied with it.

The ending was the hardest part of the story to write. In the 2018 version I'd changed the title to the same one as Stanislavski's famous book for actors, and added the tagline acknowledging there is a famous book with that title. I still hadn't added the mini movie scene in the story, but the idea that it probably would work and might be good had occurred to me.

So I wrote the ending again, probably for about the 50th time. I thought I was at the ending with her happy. But just a plain old happy ending didn't get it for me; I wanted it to be ambiguous, uncertain, and then, going back and forth with the writer Patricia DeLois, I hit on the idea that she snaps out of actress mode back into the reality of what she's doing. In one draft of the story, I thought I'd change the physical setting (have them turn into a side street where he'd parked his car) to give a setting and tonal change to provide a clue to her change in perspective. It's not great but it was the best I could do at the time. As Picasso once said, it doesn't have to be a masterpiece to get the idea across.

I did that and then, in a later version, the turn into the side street is no longer there. The story was basically over. (In the final version, I reworked the ending for probably the 100th time, and got it so that it pretty much works, I think, and strangely comes back to resonate with Stanislavski's technique.)

Let me mention one other thing. Writers often use the "cut" change of scene device. This is a double space, a couple asterisks, double space. I wanted to do this story without that device, which is, if you think about it, maybe over-used. So I wrote transitions that don't do that.

I did take wrong turns during the writing. I think the major one was I gave Nikki a roommate, and the day after the bedroom scene Nikki tells her what happened, and they talk. Then, I don't know, I guess God reached down and tapped me on the shoulder and told me I didn't need it. No, actually the roommate turned into a very strong character and the whole thing started to go off in another direction. So the roomy came out.

That's more or less how the story came about. Roughly.

I always thought the story was a pretty good one, but I couldn't get it published. This surprised me, since the Harvey

Weinstein story was in the news. Finally I realized there's not a lot of editors who want to publish a story about a b.j. and then have their friends say, "Ha ha, you published a story about a b.j." I started sending the story out in 2017 to four publications, and a few more in 2018. Finally *Weber: The Contemporary West* accepted it, but scheduled it for a year ahead. Then there was another year's delay, so it wasn't until the Spring/Summer issue of 2021 that it was published.

One final note: I don't remember where or how I stumbled across the Naughty Girl lyric, but when I researched it, I found out it's from *A Greek Slave*, a musical comedy in two acts, libretto by Owen Hall, lyrics by Harry Greenbank and Adrian Ross, music by Sidney Jones, additional numbers by Lionel Monckton, produced by George Edwardes at Daly's Theatre, London June 8, 1898 for a run of 349 performances, closing June 2, 1899. In 2015, Palala Press published hardcover and paperback editions of *A Greek Slave* (ISBN-10 1342294610 and ISBN-13 978-1342294616) and stated: "This work is in the public domain in the United States of America, and possibly other nations. Within the United States, you may freely copy and distribute this work, as no entity (individual or corporate) has a copyright on the body of the work."

Resonance is What You Want in Your Title

Hang out for a while on an internet writing site, and you're likely to see a post from someone having trouble finding a title.

A few years ago, I was lucky enough to run across a blog post by best-selling international thriller writer Barry Eisler on the subject of titles. I've been recommending it to colleagues ever since.

Everything Barry had to say about titles was both insightful and rang true for me. So I asked him if I could reprint his article here, and he graciously agreed. So here it is, Barry Eisler on titles.

The most important quality of a title is resonance: that is, "the ability to evoke or suggest images, memories, and emotions." Resonance matters because resonance makes things stick. Without it, a title produces no emotion—it stands for nothing and is instantly (and rightly) forgotten. The resonant title, by contrast, beckons you, it insidiously hooks you, it provides the first step in a seduction that culminates in the pleasure of the book itself.

There are two kinds of resonance: automatic, and acquired. They're not mutually exclusive. Let's examine both.

Automatic resonance exists in a title that moves you before you've read, or even heard anything about, the book. The title taps into something that already exists in your mind: an experience, an archetype, a memory, a famous phrase or line of poetry. The title stirs that preexisting thing to life, and in doing so makes you feel you know something important and appealing about the underlying work.

One way of checking whether a title has automatic resonance is to ask someone who has never heard of the book, "What do you think it's about?" If the person has a sense, a feeling, if the person can grasp the broad emotional contours of the story, the title has resonance. If you get a giant "huh?" in response, something is wrong. (If the title tells too much, you have a different problem—more on that below.)

Recently I heard of a book called "Cemetery of the Nameless." I'd never even heard of the book, but the title alone gave me a shiver. I couldn't tell you the plot, but my guess is, emotionally we're talking about something having to do with death, being forgotten, masses of anonymous people... perhaps, ultimately, loneliness and despair. "Motherless Brooklyn," by Jonathan Lethem, was another one that hit me instantly. Presumably the story takes place in Brooklyn, but an unmoored Brooklyn, a Brooklyn that grew up fending for itself, a Brooklyn of the disenfranchised and the dispossessed. "The Blade Itself," by Marcus Sakey, was another: a story about violence, and violence's allure. David Morrell's last two titles, each consisting of a single word, have been right on the money. "Creepers" and "Scavenger." Think they're love stories? Coming of age? Or are they stories driven by fear and suspense?

Resonance requires hitting a sweet spot, a note that lies somewhere between the hopelessly vague and the embarrassingly literal. Vague doesn't work because it tells the potential reader too little. For example, "Rain Fall" was a bad title for my first book (I didn't know better at the time). The phrase is too common, and the phenomenon it describes too ordinary, to offer any automatic resonance. Certainly it fails the "What do you think the book is about?" test (even if it passes, it's misleading—rain fall has gentle connotations, while assassin John Rain is anything but). But be careful not to go too far in the other direction: one of the titles my publisher favored for a more recent installment in my series was "The Quiet Assassin." Something as literal (and redundant) as that can't give you an emotional sense of the story. It's really no different from "Novel About An Assassin"—which is exactly the response you'd get, no more, no less, from someone in response to the "What do you think it's about?" test.

Like everyone else, Hollywood makes mistakes, but when they're on, oh, man, do they nail resonance in movie taglines. One of the best ever was "Alien": "In space, no one can hear you scream." Pause for a moment. Pretend you never saw the movie; you're hearing about it now for the first time. What do you think it's about? "Mortal terror alone in space, probably with a monster" would be my guess. But then why not just call the movie something like that? "Mortal Terror Alone in Space: Stalked by a Predatory Alien." Because resonance requires that you make the connection yourself. If someone else makes it for you, the result has all the emotional impact of a joke you didn't get until someone explained it to you. Now you get it, fine, but you never laughed, did you? We intuitively understand the problem with being too literal (although the intuition doesn't always prevent mistakes). Getting too literal is obvious; obvious feels silly; silly feels like parody. It's not a coincidence that "Airplane," "Scary Movie," "Date Movie," etc. are all comedies. And "Snakes on a Plane" was a giant wink at the audience.

Alternatively, the Alien producers could have gone for something vaguer: "Space Danger" as a title; "Fear" as a tagline. Pause again: why was what the producers chose infinitely better than a more literal or a vaguer approach? The principles you tease out will apply to titles, too.

Of course, titles are part of the overall book packaging, and the impact of a title will change when it's combined with artwork. But ideally, the title will produce resonance on its own. If it doesn't, your susceptibility to word of mouth advertising will be reduced, because someone hearing about a book for the first time from a friend can't see, and therefore isn't affected by, the artwork on the cover.

2

In the System

THE CAR IS TOTALLY CHERRY.

So is the night. A warm Southern California summer night.

I've got my elbow out the window of the pinstriped, midnight-blue Mercury Marquis with the dipped front end when the lightbar on the cop car behind me goes off red-blue-red-blue-red-blue, and they whoop the siren.

I'm downtown and they're pulling me over for being a *paisa* with a ponytail in a gangbang car on the white folks' street at the wrong time.

But I'm cool. It's routine hassle.

I hadn't done nothin'. Javier told me go ahead take the Merc. I'm such a numbnuts I go for it when Javier says he's borrowed the ride from a guy he knows. Except the guy he knows boosted it from another guy who reported it stolen.

The cops do the usual: one of them on the sidewalk back from the rear bumper, his hand on his gun butt; the younger one comes up to the window with a hand on the butt of his too.

The fuckers never pronounce it right and sometimes laugh when I tell them my name is Angel Jesus Soto, so I just say

Angelo Joseph and let it go at that. Some days I'd rather be Italian than *vato* anyway.

I give him my best smile and the Italian version of my name and keep my hands in plain sight on the top of the wheel, and he says, "Step out of the car please."

My stomach sinks. They only tell you to step out of the car when you're in the shit.

Out on the pavement I assume the stance, hands on hood, legs spread.

It's a busy street and I'm pulled over next to a hydrant, the squad car double-parked behind me, the light bar pin-balling. The sidewalk is crowded with people coming out of theaters, going into brightly lighted restaurants. Mostly they don't look and walk fast because you never know if the brown boy bent over the gangster car might go berserk. I wish I was on the sidewalk too. My eyes are wet, but I don't let on.

The younger cop pats me down while his partner, a careful distance away, snaps his holster open.

The cop finds my license.

"Real name, Angel Jesus Soto. What the hell you doing, *Angelo Joseph*, giving a peace officer false ID?"

I turn my head thinking I can explain, and before I know it he's got my arm in a lock, my face planted on the Merc's hood and the other arm back there, and he's snapping on the cuffs. I've got to give him credit, he's like a snake with the cuffs.

And that's it. I'm back in the system.

They book me, put me in the orange jumpsuit, and stick me in an isolation cell, not with the population like I expected.

"How about my phone call?" I ask the guard as he shoves me in. I figure to call Javier and at least tell him what happened to me and the Merc.

"Shut up," the guard says. "No phone, no contacts."

I flake out on the thin pad, wondering what the hell. Has the system changed that much since I was here the last time?

They've got me stuck away. I listen to the hollow sound of concrete and steel. A TV somewhere isn't loud enough to follow, a murmur of men's voices, the occasional laugh; the tang of disinfectant; a whiff of cigarette smoke; the fug where too many men sweated out too much time.

I drift and wonder did Javier know the Merc was jacked when he offered it? I go back over the easy way he said it: "Nah, don't bother," he said, "take that Merc over there." Hard as I try, I can't read anything into it, but that don't mean there wasn't nothing there.

My mind moves to Rubytips like it does when I get sleepy. Javier's sister, Elena, she's fifteen, Rubytips is her Tweet handle. It's just a tag until you see her titties. I'm at Javier's house as much as my own, and Elena is always around. I knew she had something going on. I try not to look, but who can't notice? Then one day we're alone and she asks me if I want to see them and pulls up her top. I'm sitting in a kitchen chair and she's standing in front of me and I'm looking at the most beautiful set of tits I could ever imagine. I can see why she's proud of them. They're nice size, high and pointy, perfect, with bright pink nipples.

"Want to touch?" she asks.

They're warm silk.

From then on, whenever we're alone—and she's making things happen that way—off comes her blouse or up comes her shirt. I kiss them and pet them. But that's all. I never touch her down below. She puts a hand on my Levi's and rubs and squeezes, but I don't let her inside my pants. I'd be lost for sure.

I know what's going on. Her homeys are having babies, some of them getting married, and she wants to hang with them. She's picked me out of the lineup.

I'm on the edge of sleep in that cell, petting the rubytips, and then my eyes pop open and I'm sitting up remembering a couple months ago when Javier walked in on us. Elena and I are on the sofa with the TV going and I'm stroking her beauties and Javier opens the door and starts to walk in. He backs out, closes the door and never says nothing about it, so I don't bring it up either. I worry for a week or two, but nothing changes and it fades away.

But now I see it. You won't be touching my sister's titties, not where you're going.

The next afternoon I'm chained to a steel table in an interview room. When they came for me, they put manacles on my ankles, my hands cuffed to a waist chain, my ankles chained to my waist and I say, "What the hell?" and one of the guards kicks me in the shin with a steel-toe boot and it hurts like hell and I shut up.

My public defender sits beside me; across from us is the assistant district attorney. The PD goes first. He's got my file open in front of him and pages through it with his right hand. He's maybe thirty-five, tall and trim, a clean sharp look to his face, broad shoulders, thinning hair. His left hand is in the pocket of this dark blue suit jacket, and I can see it in there flexing on a rubber ball he carries. This morning when he talked to me in my cell he had it out, squeezing it and flipping it from hand to hand. He told me about his weight lifting and his surfing. "The human body is a temple," he said.

Now he's going through my file. "Knowingly providing false information to a peace officer," he says, "grand theft auto, resisting arrest, accepting stolen goods with intent." He looks up at me. "If you're convicted, felony strike two."

They always throw in resisting arrest, that's routine. The stolen goods is the stuff in the Merc's trunk I didn't know about. The strike two sends a shiver down my spine. It's three strikes and you're out. On the third strike, doesn't matter what, they put you away twenty-five to life. My first strike was seven years ago, when I was eighteen, B&E, breaking and entering. I was the lookout on the corner for Javier and a couple guys, that's all, never even went in the store. I've been clean since. Doesn't matter.

But having two strikes... Everybody knows about the drunk

coming out of a bar, finds a bike in a front yard, rides it home. Strike three, twenty-five to life for riding a kid's bicycle home in the middle of the night.

Two strikes is like having a guy walking backwards in front of you twenty-four seven with the point of a knife at your throat: one stumble and you're dead.

The ADA speaks up. She's younger than the PD, but it won't be long before she's older, a twisted, worn look to her face, dark hair short in a man's cut, gray suit. "Not *if* you're convicted," she says, "*when*." She makes clear she's got more balls than the pussy PD.

She's right. The PD shrugs and smiles. "You need to cut a deal." He slides the file across to the ADA and stands up. "I need a break."

I watch him saunter out the door. What the fuck? I need a break? He walks out? Then I catch on: he doesn't want to know.

My shin aches as the ADA puts her palms flat on the table and lays it out, the trial she's got going on, the guy she needs to put away big time.

It comes down to this: I do my part and I walk, the arrest record expunged, no strike two, no nothing. A window of blue sky opens somewhere up above me and I nod my head, looking up at that little bit of sky.

They keep the shackles on me, transport me to the County Courthouse, and jerk me into a windowless room with just one cop. Before I know what's what, he hits me twice across the face with his baton, forehand and backhand, zap zap.

These fucking cops, are they faster and harder, or am I slower and softer? Are they all vets from Afghanistan or what?

The holding cells are in the basement and they pitch me on the bed, weak-kneed and woozy, take off the shackles, and toss me a towel for the blood dripping from my mouth. I know what it's about, a reputation for the new guy, a badass who needs to be subdued.

As my head clears, I look through the bars to the next cell and check him out, the guy who's on trial.

He's flat on his back on the floor in the middle of his cell, ankles crossed, fingers laced behind his head. On his throat, just above the collar of his orange jumpsuit, I can see the tatt of black fingers sticking up, and I know there's an M in the palm of that black hand. *La eMe.*

"Hey, man," I say.

He turns his head; his black eyes open on me like radar. He's got two tear drops tattooed at the corner of an eye. His lips barely move when he talks. "Shut the fuck up, *ese*."

I try a couple more times, but he won't talk, he won't turn his head or open his eyes. He's a soldier. He ignores the bed, stays on the floor to show he's harder than anything they've got in here. Harder than concrete. Harder than steel.

All night long, he won't speak. He's way out ahead of the ADA.

Shit, he was *born* so far ahead of the butch ADA she'll never catch up. It's funny when I lay there and think about it, but not funny ha-ha. He doesn't give a shit and he has no doubts. Warriors don't doubt; they don't wonder should I do this, should I do that. He'll be as much at home in a cell as he would be in his mama's kitchen.

In a way, I wish I was like him. It would be simpler not to want anything, not hope for anything. But we aren't like that. Elena with her rubytips wants a baby and maybe a husband; the PD wants a paycheck so he can keep surfing and lifting; the ADA wants a conviction, she's desperate for a conviction. And now I'm desperate too.

The ADA told me what she'll need when she puts me on the stand in the morning.

"It doesn't have to be a full confession. I'll ask you if you spoke to him during the night and you say you asked him if it's true he did the girl in the shower so there wouldn't be DNA. All I need is he smiled and nodded. That's all I need. Corroboration."

One lightweight lie and I walk. But I know what happens next: *La eMe* puts a green light on me and everybody in my family, maybe Javier and Elena too. *La eMe* is like an army, guys everywhere. A green light means drive-bys, blood in the streets. Or I tell the truth: the fucking warrior told me to shut the fuck up and never said nothing else all night long. Then I'm the one looking at a cell—there's no doubt of that—and I come out with two strikes.

The clock is ticking and I've got to choose.

Characterization and
Character Arc in "System"

This story was first published online by *The Uprising Review* under my Scribophile pen name, Carlos Dunning. Later *Uprising* decided to specialize in science fiction, fantasy and horror, and my story wasn't up on their site anymore. After Rick Taubold at *Fabula Argentea* (Latin for silver story) had published another of my stories, I asked him if he'd be interested in publishing *In the System,* and he accepted it.

This story was a lot easier to write than *Actor,* I don't remember working that hard on it, don't remember revising it much, though I'm sure I did, so I was surprised when it was accepted by the first publication I sent it to, both times.

One of the editors at *Uprising* told me that what they'd particularly liked about the story were the characterizations. Before he said that, it had never occurred to me that the characterizations were anything other than routine.

Looking at the story today, I notice that the characterizations are brief and specific. Years before I wrote the story, I played golf occasionally with an attorney who worked for the Public Defender Office. Like the character in the story, he lifted

36

and surfed, and he once mentioned that he thought the human body was a temple, and it stuck in my mind. But there the similarity between the real person and the character ends. The description of the Assistant District Attorney I made up out of whole cloth.

Because of who Angel Jesus [AHN-hell HAY-soos] is, a young guy without a lot of education, the descriptions needed to be succinct and to the point, the sort of things he would notice. I think perhaps this has a lot to do with how they work in the story.

Ever since California passed the three strikes sentencing law in 1994, I wanted to write something critical of it, it's just so knee-jerk stupid. The law was modified in 2012 by referendum, so it's not quite so draconian, but it's still dumb.

The United States is the world leader in incarceration, despite the national incarceration rate being at its lowest in 20 years, with about 25% of the world's prison population being in the US, the land of the free.

There are 1.8 million people locked up in the United States, and what efforts are being made to educate and rehabilitate these people? What are their prospects when they are released? The United States has some of the highest recidivism rates in the world. According to the National Institute of Justice, almost 44% of criminals released return before the first year out of prison.

These are people, human beings. They aren't being sentenced to prison, they're being sentenced to a grim future without a lot of hope in it. It's such a wasteful and dispiriting revolving door.

But back to the story.

I think the key to the story is the first thing that might be called a characterization of Angel Jesus:

The sidewalk is crowded with people coming out of theaters, going into brightly lighted restaurants. Mostly they don't look and walk fast because you never know if the brown boy bent over the gangster car might go berserk. I wish I was on the sidewalk too. My eyes are wet, but I don't let on.

I had come across the moniker Rubytips somewhere online, and my imagination turned the name into the character. The same thing happened to me with another character, the online avatar transforming into a character in a story. We'll get to that one later on. The situation with Rubytips explains why Angel Jesus is in this situation in the first place, and makes him even more a victim of circumstances.

I think the thing that sells the story at the end, really tightens the reader into the plausibility, is the one word: *corroboration*. For me, it seems to chime like a death knell.

I've been interested in Spanish ever since, years ago, I read *The Ordinary Seaman*, a wonderful novel by Francisco Goldman. Come to think of it, there are parallels between the protagonist of that story, Esteban, and Angel Jesus in mine. They are both victims of circumstance.

But the use of *ese* in my story had another origin. Back in the 1960s, when we were playing the Synanon Game in what was once a grocery store on Fourth Avenue in San Diego, Al Velasco and his wife (I forget her name) came by to play the game. They wanted to work out some relationship squabble. During the game, Al kept calling his wife *ese*, and from the endearing way he used it, I assumed it was a pet name between them. Finally she sat up straight in her chair, pissed off, and said, "Stop calling me *that*." Which is, of course, the literal meaning of the word, though it has a number of connotations.

Character Arc

The characterizations in the story are apparent, but does Angel Jesus undergo a character arc? In the traditional and prevalent notion of a character arc, the character must change in some way, at least, if you asked around that might be the consensus you'd get. I think this definition is too rigid. Looked at that way, Angel Jesus is the same from beginning to end.

But don't look at it that way; look at it from the point of view of the reader. Throughout the story, the reader's understanding of Angel Jesus is being enlarged and altered. (Let me be honest about it: I didn't know what I was doing. It came right out of my intuition.)

Why was it in my intuition in the first place? Because I'd been spending years trying to figure out how to write stories. (This is another basis for the old dictum, you can learn to write, but no one can teach you to write, i.e., no one can fill your intuition with the stuff that needs to be there, only you can do that.)

So don't think about *character arc* only in terms of the character changing, also think of it in terms of the *reader's perception* of the character changing. Each time Angel understands something more about his situation or characterizes one of the other people in the story, the reader's understanding and appreciation of Angel alters, if only slightly, though the reader probably isn't consciously aware of this happening. But it's there, on a feeling level, for the reader.

Perception is Inference

What is there in the description of the assistant attorney general in the story *In the System* that makes it work?

As a reminder, here's the description:

She's younger than the public defender, but it won't be long before she's older, a twisted, worn look to her face, dark hair short in a man's cut, gray suit.

There isn't much there, a vague general reference to her look, short dark hair, gray suit. And yet despite this paucity of detail, in your mind's eye, chances are good you have a fairly complete picture of this person.

Why do you see in your mind's eye so much more than is there on the page?

I knew that this happened with descriptions, that they convey quite a bit more than the words on the page might justify, but I didn't know why. I knew the descriptions in the novels by one of my favorite writers, Donald E. Westlake, were brief and pointed and worked beautifully, but I didn't understand how he managed it so consistently.

Then I came across an article called *The Itch* by Atul Gawande, M.D., the physician who writes for the *New Yorker*. It was in the June 30, 2008 issue, and described the medical condition of a woman with an uncontrollable itch on her scalp. The article goes into her medical history and the attempts at treatment, which all failed. To skip to the end of the article, and the point I want to make, it's because the itch isn't on her skin or in her nerves leading to her scalp, it was happening in the neurons of her brain.

The old theory of perception, we feel what we touch, we see what's out there, this is a logic that's always seemed unassailable. Science is now finding out this isn't at all how it works.

If you look at a tree in a clearing you will have a notion of the details of its bark, the roundness of the trunk, details that we perceive instantly. But what's going through your optic nerve from your eye is a distorted, two-dimensional image with areas missing. What scientists have found when they look at the brain's primary visual cortex is that only twenty percent of the information is coming from the retina, the rest of it is coming from other parts of the brain, including memory.

One scientist has estimated that visual perception is more than ninety percent memory and less than ten percent sensory nerve signals. To sum it up, *perception is inference*. You aren't seeing what's out there; you're seeing what's out there expanded and elaborated on by everything in your brain that relates to what you think you're seeing out there. When you watch a movie or television or the NFL, you think you're seeing people move. That's not what's on the screen. What you're seeing are still pictures running at 24 or 30 frames per second. With only 20 milliseconds between frames, your brain can't help seeing things as continuous motion, so that's what you perceive, and if asked under oath, you'd swear the images are moving.

Even when the information we get is vague, a figure of speech, a man's haircut, a gray suit, our brains produce a rich, three-dimensional image that we believe we can almost see.

One of the most amazing things about it is that it's a hard-wired process, we can't help it, we can't keep from seeing in our mind's eye the images that the words evoke.

Seal.

See? It just happened to you and you couldn't help it. You are unable to see the word as a word, you had to *read* it, and when you read it, you saw in your mind the animal represented by the word, unless you happen to be someone who works with adhesives, grommets, washers, gaskets or something related to sealing things up, or maybe you saw an imprint of a royal signature or a Japanese document. Not everybody has the same stuff going on in their brains.

You write a brief description, touching only the high points, just a brushstroke or two, and the reader's mind immediately creates a complete picture, fills in the rest automatically. Not just some rough sketch, but color, sound, texture and *meaning*, yes even meaning gets automatically provided by the brains of your readers. You have an understanding of not just how she looks, but the whole personality of that assistant district attorney.

It's very difficult to look at words on a page and just see them without reading them. This is why back in the old days professional proofreaders would read a piece backwards, start at the end and go backward, word by word. Judging by the number of typos I see in published books, I'm not sure they do that anymore.

Perception is inference. That's how description works.

A Unified Theory of Excess
Baggage and Transparency

Ever read the advice that whatever doesn't move the story forward shouldn't be there?

Here's how it strikes me.

To write well, you have no choice but to be two people. You need to be the writer, but then on the other hand, you need to be your typical reader ("your" meaning the reader you are specifically writing for).

I know that right away some writers are going to start yammering that they are not writing for a reader at all, they are writing for THEMSELVES, they write to please themselves only, not some nimrod browsing the graphic novel shelves at Barnes & Noble. Okay, okay, okay. Do we have to go over that ground again? Isn't the writer, in that case, writing for the reader who is his or her ownself? And now some ink-spattered hand will go up and a young person with dandruff on his glasses and a copy of *Ectoplasm* sticking out of his bib overalls will remark that, in the interests of a more pure artistic endeavor, his goal is to write a novel that he, personally, finds completely boring and uninteresting, and this certainly disproves right from the git-go what was just said.

At this point it's only sensible to have the sergeant at arms take the young person in question out to the courtyard, stand him up against the wall and admonish him, saving us all a bit of argument.

Some writers can only be one person at a time. First they write and then some period of time later they can take the manuscript out of the drawer and pretend to be the typical reader and start revising. Others (and I think this tends to happen, if it ever does, after lots and lots of writing) can handle both roles more or less at the same time without having the internal editor overwhelm and inhibit the writer (generally the cause of what's often called writer's block).

The key thing in this writer/typical reader interaction is that the typical reader needs to be imperceptibly led along the narrative trail by a lead rope that (key point) always *seems to* (but doesn't really, it's an illusion) have some slack in it.

Did you ever read *The Man Who Listens to Horses: The Story of a Real-Life Horse Whisperer?* I'm talking about Monty Roberts, not Robert Redford. Monty found that if he stood in a certain way a wild horse would amble over and stand behind his shoulder, in effect "link-up" with the whisperer. Then the whisperer could walk around the corral and the wild horse would tag along.

That's what good narrative does. The opening sets something in motion that generates in the reader a flicker of curiosity that causes her to want to know more about whatever it is you've started (the inclination to link-up, sometimes called the willing suspension of disbelief, combined with a little curiosity). And then the next sentence is both responsive to that flicker of curiosity and causes the reader to be interested... and yes, there it is in the next paragraph, something that satisfies the curiosity and something else the reader wants to know, and the reader thinks, "This is getting good."

It's when the writer does anything other than this that problems like overwriting, digressing, getting wordy, self-indulgence, purple prose, etc. crop up. These are all ways of saying "it doesn't work for me." The fundamental transaction that the typical reader desires isn't taking place the way the typical reader wants it to. It's as if the writer arbitrarily decides this is what I want to stick in at this point, or I really need to get this stuff in at this point, ignoring the prior expectations (if any) that have been set up in the typical reader's mind. The typical reader doesn't like this. It's not what the typical reader signed up for.

When the writer is acting like the horse whisperer, when the typical reader is being gently led through the story but isn't aware of the lead rope much less the halter, then that's what I think of as *transparency*—it's as if the text almost isn't even there and the typical reader is caught up in simply watching the story unroll in her mind's eye.

There's also transparency in drawing and painting. Robert Henri (1865-1929) writing in *The Art Spirit* in 1923 wrote:

Look at this drawing by Rembrandt.
[There are no drawings in the book.]
Your mind is at once engaged by the life of the person represented. The beauty of the lines of the drawing rest in the fact that you do not realize them as lines, but are only conscious of what they state of the living person.

That's transparency, when you read a bit of exposition, description or dialogue, and you don't realize them as words on a page, but are only aware of what they say about the character or scene that is alive in your mind, that is the beauty of good writing.

If you want to make your writing beautiful, make it transparent.

This is true even when the writing on the page is clearly

beautiful when taken out of context. For example, take this simile: *Guitar notes struck the air like silver dimes.* It's beautiful because it's so perfect—guitar notes do somehow strike the air like silver dimes, in some crazy way that makes sense. And the line is beautiful because it's unique, something we've never thought of before. And the line is also beautiful because it fits so exquisitely within the scene in which it occurs, which happens to be in William Styron's first novel *Lie Down in Darkness.*

It's when the writer tries to make the writing beautiful without regard to the context of the story that we get purple prose.

The dreaded adverbs fall into this theory.

"You have no chance with me," she said sneeringly.

It's as if the writer doesn't think the typical reader is going to get the idea from the dialogue alone, and so tightens up the lead rope and gives the typical reader a jerk along the trail, causing the typical reader to roll his eyes. Give the typical reader enough jerks on the lead rope and the typical reader puts down the book.

That seems to me to be the fundamental process in learning to write—learning to stand in the reader's shoes and look back at the text and see how it plays for the typical reader. That's the essential skill. I know my saying this will make some writers crazy. They just cannot tolerate the notion that some nobody from nowhere is going to read their stuff and render a judgment. Of course this circles back to the writing-for-myself argument mentioned above. I have no problem with someone who wants to write only for his or her self. Fine, do it. But don't go posting your manuscript on some board for others to read. The act of doing that is an admission that you are (despite your protests) writing for readers, and welcome to the septic tank along with the rest of us.

But back to the adverbs. In the interests of scholarship and research, here's 44 words taken from a published novel that is pretty amazing:

He could feel himself grinning sillily like he always did when he was in pain and he had to choke back a hunger to laugh.

"I'll give you another sedative, if you want," Alma said.

"I don't much like them things," he grinned sillily.

In the next two exchanges, the character uses *grinned sillily* twice more.

The novel was a runaway best-seller. Maybe more surprising: It won the National Book Award and was ranked number 62 on Modern Library's list of Best 20th Century Novels. The movie of the novel won eight Academy Awards including Best Picture.

The book: *From Here to Eternity*. It's a great read.

Certainly editorial criteria have changed since 1951 when the book was published. But this also might lead you to consider the proposition that yes, it's about the writing, but maybe it's even more about the storytelling.

3

What I Done

Scientists and other brilliant and serious adults assume that if we ever get visitors from another planet they'll be like them— brilliant and serious adults. But what if they turn out to be dorky guys just goofing around?

I BURIED MY HEART OUT BEHIND THE SHED.

I mean, I had to do something with it. When I took it out it was way more messy than I expected. Those bastards never mentioned that.

And it didn't look at all like anything I'd ever seen on a valentine. I never thought to ask them what it would look like or what should I do with it and they hadn't told me.

It dripped all over the table and floor, so I didn't think about it, just slopped it in a saucepan since I was in the kitchen to start with. I guess I could have put it in the sink but there was already a stack of dirty dishes sitting there, silverware on top.

So there it sat in a saucepan on the sideboard and the damn thing kept beating. They should have told me about that too. They should have said oh, don't be surprised if it keeps on beating. And I would have asked them why it did that. But they never said and I never had the chance to ask and they were gone.

But mostly I would have asked them what the hell I was supposed to do with it once I had it out, and what was I supposed to do without it. I mean without having it inside me. I poured a cup of coffee and sat at the kitchen table and puzzled over that question and listened to it beat.

The beating got to be damned annoying. It was my grandmother's kitchen, hadn't been nothing done to it since Ike was in the White House and everything was pretty beat-up, and the dented old saucepan didn't sit level, and what with the beating heart the saucepan was rocking back and forth and making a noise like a crinkly old clock or something. It got to be damned annoying.

So after a while I took the saucepan out to the shed, grabbed a shovel and buried it, the whole thing, drippy beating heart, saucepan, the both of 'em.

I went back in the house thinking I'd done pretty good, thinking I'd figured things out for myself, done what needed doing.

I hadn't been sitting long at the kitchen table when they come back, zooming up the cinder drive the way they done before in their fancy silver thing looked like it was out of a TV movie.

The three of 'em come prancing in the kitchen on their little five legs like they done before with their big saucer-size eyes bulging out and those funny doo-dads sticking out on their heads, nodding and saying hi and all just like they done before.

Where the hell you been, I asked 'em, kinda rude, but then I'd been under a certain amount of strain, everything that'd been going on while they were gone, the questions I'd had and all. I felt like they'd left me in the lurch.

Been over to the next farm down the road, they said, trying to talk some hick farmer into taking out his heart, they said, and they turned to each other, laughing. It wasn't laughing the way we laugh, but I could tell all right how it was meant.

I done it, I told them. I done took it out and put it in my grandma's saucepan, slick as anything.

Oh yeah, they said, then where is it, show it to us.

When I told them what I'd done with it they laughed and laughed and laughed, all doubled over laughing with big tears rolling down their funny little faces. They would tail off on the laughing then one or the other of them would say buried it and they'd all start in again. Then they'd tire of it and one of them would say behind the shed and that would set them to going again.

It torqued me, it torqued me real bad, being made fun of like that. I could see they thought I was just a hick farmer. So I stepped outside the kitchen door, grabbed that good old garden spade and come back in and laid waste to those damn laughing aliens or whatever the hell they were. It wasn't long till my grandmother's kitchen was a hell of a mess of what I guess that green stuff was blood and gooey insides a bunch of different colors. But I felt pretty good about it, so I shoveled the whole mess into my grandpap's wheelbarrow and went out and buried that behind the shed too. Stood over that mound of fresh turned dirt and dusted my hands, job well done.

If that'd been an end to it, all to the good. But their damn vehicle was right in the middle of the drive, and there wasn't no way I was going to get the F-150 around it without cutting some fence on one end, driving out in the pasture, then cutting another stretch of fence on the other end of that damn thing, which they'd even left the lights on inside of it.

I thought on it a bit, and concluded there wasn't no way I was going to cut a perfectly good fence over a bunch of damn aliens from outer space, and I come up with the answer.

I went out and fired up the backhoe. I put the bucket up high as it would go and drove the tractor up against that alien vehicle and put in the clutch and let the bucket drop full weight. That's a thirty-inch cold-rolled steel bucket that weighs in around four-hundred pounds. The car or spaceship or whatever the hell it was had looked all streamlined and slick before I started, but I soon found out it wasn't no match for a Case backhoe with a thirty-inch bucket. It took me about an hour to get that silver thing mashed down pretty good. There weren't no lights shining in it by the time I got done.

I went in the house and dialed up Walter Becket who runs the junkyard over outside Gilman.

When I told him I had a job of work, Walter said yeah goddamnit Niles what the hell you got going on?

I said jump in that deuce and a half flatbed and get your sorry ass out here and I'll show you.

Walter and me talked that way to one another. We knowed each other since about the third grade so we didn't stand on no ceremony.

I fixed me some supper and about an hour and a half later I heard beep beep beep Walter come backing up the drive. By the time I got out there Walter was standing at the back of his truck the same confounded look he'd had on his face all through algebra, one gloved hand holding the cable end he'd unspooled from the winch, the other tucked up inside the top of his bib overalls.

Walter said what the hell you got here Niles?

He had no head for algebra, but Walter could get squinty-eyed and figure on things, all right. Now that I looked at that space ship thing the way Walter saw it, I realized the mistake I'd made.

Dropped out of the sky, I said. Probably come off a plane or maybe one of them satellites.

Walter said yeah sure. Dropped right in the middle of your driveway neat as a pin. Then that backhoe sitting there went right to work on it all by itself.

Damn. Walter'd seen right through me. So I told him the whole thing, how it happened.

Well I tell you, Walter said, I'll get you off the hook, Niles. I'll tote this thing over to the yard and stick it in the back somewhere. But you better check your hole card. You should never a done in them critters, no matter how bad they was ragging on you. And you never should a squashed this thing up like you done. You should a called Robbie over in Onarga and asked him about it.

Robbie was our Agricultural Agent.

He was right, dammit. That wasn't me at all. Normally I wouldn't a done any of that stuff. Hell, I carry spiders outdoors and put 'em on the lilac bush. What'd come over me? Only thing I could figure, I didn't have a heart no more. I told myself, Niles, from here on out you're gonna have to think twice about things. And what the hell you gonna tell the doc next time he sticks that thing on your chest and listens? He's gonna be one surprised son of a bitch.

Notes on "What I Done"

The story was originally written as an entry into a weekly flash fiction contest at the online writing site I was participating in at the time. The contest gave the starting phrase, "I buried my heart..." and the story was to go on from there, limit 1,000 words. Of course what came to mind was the title of the well-known book *I Buried My Heart at Wounded Knee*.

My entry didn't win, dammit!

But I liked it, so I added another 400 or so words to the original 1,000, came up with what I considered a dynamite tagline, and the story was accepted by the third publication I sent it to, *Furtive Dalliance, Issue 01, Spring 2018*.

I didn't get the tagline for the story until I was well into the revision to a longer form and I think it's the tagline that sells it as much as the story itself. It's a provocative idea, the visitors from outer space resembling my old high school buddies, Bunbury Mutual No. 1 we called ourselves, goofing around just for laughs.

From the first, I pictured the protagonist sitting at the kitchen table at my grandparents' farm, which was about 90 miles south of Chicago. The farmhouse, which I understand burned down some years ago, must have been built around the turn of the century or before, and I mean the turn from the 19th to the 20th. When I first visited it, at the age of 9 or 10, the kitchen sink had a pump with a handle. When you pumped it, you got cold water from the well. The telephone had a crank you turned when you wanted the operator, and it was on a party line: if it rang three times, the call was for someone in your house. The neighbors could listen in just by lifting the handset off the hook, but it was considered bad manners, and the adults wouldn't let us kids do it, though it was so tempting when the phone rang one, two or four times.

After I finished the story, I had some ideas about how it might continue: Niles goes into Miller Wyfells seed and general home goods store in La Hogue, which was the tiny village a mile and a half up the road from the farm, where he sees Walter's daughter (the guy who runs the junkyard), age 9 or 10, with a small alien on a leash, treating it like a puppy. The little alien sees Niles, and starts to laugh at him. Niles realizes what's happened—the aliens are hatching out of the space ship he thought he destroyed. Niles stomps on the little alien, squashing it. Niles is in trouble with Walter and the sheriff, of course, but is let off with a fine. But Niles isn't finished. He knows what's left of that space ship is hatching out aliens, so he get the dynamite out of the shed, sneaks into Walter's junkyard at night, and blows the remnants of the space ship to smithereens. When asked about this far more serious crime, Niles admits it. He loses everything, the farm, what little money he has. The story ends with a scene of Niles living as a homeless person on the street in Los Angeles or San Diego, panhandling. He wears a child's plastic toy stethoscope around his neck, and offers pedestrians the opportunity to try to find his heart beat, which, he says, he hasn't got. No one takes him up on the offer.

I knew how the rest of the story would go, and that took the steam out of it for me, so I didn't bother to write the rest of it. Thinking about it now, the rest of the story seems too pat. The reader would have seen it coming a mile away.

Overwriting

Here's a question someone asked on one of the online boards:

What exactly do you mean by over writing? I'm curious: I've heard it said a lot, and have always suspected it as being shorthand for just not liking a writer's style. Does it mean more flowery, too many adjectives, stuff like that? Or sentences overloaded with ideas?

I think overwriting is ubiquitous on writing sites and can refer to several causes/symptoms. Sometimes it's the use of three descriptors where one is enough. Often it's senseless and endless exaggeration; everything has to be the most, the biggest, the women beautiful beyond compare, the men completely handsome with green eyes and curly black hair, etc. Overwriting can boil down to too many adjectives and adverbs and sometimes a misperception of the audience.

Often the root cause is the writer's desire to describe whatever it is absolutely down to a gnat's eyebrow, so that the reader is forced—forced I tell you!—to see it just the way the writer wants it seen. Caving in to this desire is almost always a mistake. Stephen King has described this problem, and its cure, elsewhere online, so I won't go into a lot of detail on it here. I think it's enough to say that written narration tends to be for the most part a broad-brush medium. Often the writer only needs to *indicate* rather than describe, because each reader's mind's eye will supply (and apply) the specifics. Often the strongest writing (key point) is when the reader makes the connections in her own mind.

When the first story in this book, *An Actor Prepares*, was published, they used a still photograph from the movie *North by Northwest* to illustrate it. I understood why they did it, what they had in mind. But the photo grated on me, because it took the scene in the story between two people who weren't Cary Grant and Eva Marie Saint, which disagreed with whatever image the story had generated in the reader's mind.

Exposition is easily overdone—either too much of it or too specifically gone into. A good example of how little exposition is needed is *No Country for Old Men*. Just pick it up, or use the Look Inside feature on Amazon, and start reading from the beginning, slowly and carefully, noticing the words on the page and comparing them to the pictures that form in your mind. You'll notice how little exposition there is on the page, and how that sparse prose creates a full picture in your head. That is exactly why too much doesn't work.

But overwriting, its causes and cures, can be more compli-cated. When reading someone's manuscript, it's difficult to sepa-rate out what is consciously intentional on the part of the writer from what just happens to arrive at the point at which the writer needed something, i.e., what's more toward the organic-intuitive vs. the artificial-intellectual end of the spectrum. There are those things that are written down in full awareness and the stuff that comes from habit, the writer's more-or-less unexamined proclivi-ties and tendencies, and we all have them. One of the things it seems like I've found out is that until one becomes aware of it, the basics of one's personality patterns tend to get superimposed on the characters and their interactions without the writer being fully aware of it. I think this is particularly true of the writer's personal modes of handling emotional issues and behavior. Maybe you can see it in my stories in this collection: Hey, Bill, the female protagonists are all tall! But wait, Ruthie is tiny, and Nikki is average height.

Maybe there are two issues involved. One is the writer's lack of awareness that this is what he's doing—how do I relate to people in the real world and do I relate to my characters the same way? Then there is the situation for writers who haven't yet reached a point where they've got their characters over there in another part of their mind where they are characters and not in some sense "the writer" in another guise. Of course, looked at another way, everyone and everything must by definition be part of the writer (since it all comes out of his/her/their mind). Down this path lies endless back and forth, and I'm not going there; you know what I mean. Of course they're all you, but when you're more experienced (hardened? deft? facile? schizophrenic?), not that much you. To put it another way, they're you, but you can arbitrarily mess with them and make them into somebody else. The assistant district attorney isn't me at all. On the other hand, maybe she is, at least a bit—as Solzhenitsyn has said, the line between good and evil runs through every human heart.

The root cause might be a lack of confidence in the writing and a lack of understanding how fiction works its magic in the mind of the reader. Getting this right is for some people probably mostly intuitive, but I don't think it has to be kept at that level. I contend that the more conscious you make the process the better the writer you'll be. Here's a snippet of scene:

"You've got to be kidding," the hooker said.

They stood on the corner, a light drizzle turning the midnight streets to glistening blackness.

"You've got a freaking beard down to your bellybutton, and you want me to do what to you?" She laughed. "You are one sick dude!"

Take just the phrase: a light drizzle made the streets a glistening blackness. A true-life fact: This is pretty far from being an accurate description of how a dark, asphalt street really looks in a light rain. But what I was consciously aware of when I wrote it was that all I needed was a rough brushstroke or two that would get the idea across, because the picture it generates in the reader's mind is a memory of all those wonderful movie shots where they have wetted down the streets beforehand and carefully lighted them, because it makes them look so cool and dramatic. (They did the same get-the-street-wet technique in a recent episode in season 2 of *Euphoria*.) No one's mind's eye sees a real street; everyone imagines the movie image, which is so much better. I think that happens because we've all seen thousands of hours of television and movies with wet streets whether we noticed it at the time or not, but we seldom go walking in the city in the rain, or if we do, we're not paying a lot of attention to how the asphalt looks. "Gee, Main Street in the rain doesn't look anything like that street in *Night of a Million Vampires*."

What is the opposite of overwriting? I think a lot of the craft of writing well is to stay what could be called "below the line." By this I mean restrain yourself in the writing (or in the editing) process so that you allow the reader to bring his/her own images and associations to what you're doing. In the most powerful writing, the connections occur in the reader's mind. If you'd like more examples of how to do it, I always suggest finding a copy of *Lie Down in Darkness*, William Styron's first novel. It is filled with such an abundance. What you'll find is an indelible impression can be created with not a lot of words. It seems to me that *Lie Down in Darkness* comes close to the intersection of prose and poetry, and fortunately it's now available as an e-book. The novel is certainly one of a kind so far as I know. I'm unaware of any modern English-language novel that's as richly layered.

What, you haven't read it? If you're serious about writing, you should do that at some point.

Not For Everybody

An email this a.m. from a colleague referring me to an online thread with multiple posts on the use of third person vs. first person.

First person, third person, for me any argument seems silly. The writer writes it the way it seems to need to be written, and it may work for some and not for others, but that's always the way with everything. Back in the day when I was working for a living, I soon realized that about twenty percent of any reader group wasn't going to like it, no matter what it was. Stand on a street corner and hand out $20 bills. You'll find a certain percentage of the people won't go for the offer. They'll know there's some nefarious scheme involved, a hidden camera, they are going to be humiliated possibly on national TV; they refuse to be tricked.

The tense, like other conventions in fiction, tends to disappear in direct proportion to the depth of the reader's engagement in the story. Writing fiction is in one sense very much like a magic trick, the kind of magic that practitioners call close work, where the cards or coins or whatever seem to appear and vanish not on some distant stage, but right there under your nose, over a dinner table or standing at a bar. You can smell the magician's after-shave, but damned if you know how the queen of hearts turned out to be the card when you were the one that did the choosing.

To someone who knows the two-handed pass, the answer is simple (isn't the answer in both magic tricks and fiction always, more or less, simple?). The artistry is making the two-handed pass transparent, so deft it disappears. And so it is with fiction, making the story and character (always a blend as tightly wound as strands of DNA) so agile, nimble, dexterous and proficient in the telling that the language, the tense, the words and punctuation—all the elements of the two-handed pass—become transparent, disappear, and all that's left is the effect, the magic.

It doesn't matter how you do it, only that you stumble across the doorway, perhaps the one in the ivy-covered stone wall in the Hermann Hesse novel *Steppenwolf*, the entrance to the Magic Theatre, and you step through, ignoring the warning: Not For Everybody.

4

Oh I'm Really So, So Sorry (As If)

BASICALLY, OUR PROBLEM WAS THIS: where and how do we kill him?

I mean while not getting nabbed by the authorities, and also not making it into a total chore, if at all possible.

Where was simple. We looked at each other and both of us said it at the same time: *Nordstrom.*

Where else? Two seventeen-year-old high school girls figuring out our first hit job. She's Charlotte and I'm Dana.

We head for the second floor of Nordstrom in the Westgate Mall. We're killing a guy, so we're at the men's department. Charlotte goes hey, how about we get him into a fitting room? Nice and private.

I go hmm, what comes next? Say we bust into the fitting room *and then?*

Char looks at me and I look at her and we X'd out the fitting room, headed for the escalator.

We got there and it stopped me: the escalator.

It's trippy to stand at the top of an escalator and watch the steps emerge. Each steel comb slides out, turns down, and glides away, so smooth.

It's the fold that got me. Steel against steel. Hard edges. They're especially dangerous-looking if you're thinking what it would be like if some person, a guy you've decided to kill for example, tripped and somehow toppled down with the back of his neck or the back of his head right on one of those sharp steel edges.

I grabbed Charlotte's arm and made her stand at the top of the escalator and pointed to the steps, those sharp, hard, steel edges.

"Perfect!" she said. "Now all we have to do is get him here."

Nordstrom is high end. If you look up you'll notice the lighting is sort of soft, but with these spotlights—hundreds of them—focused on the counters, the racks, the display tables. Makes you want to check out the merch. Yeah, I took a good look at the ceiling thinking about cameras. After all, you don't want to kill a guy and have it caught on video. LOL.

All in all, a pretty cool place to hang while you're waiting for the dude you plan to toe-tag.

We picked Wednesday because we wanted to get it done before the creep could do any more damage, and because we figured it was a slow day at the store. Same with the time, just before noon. We've both been to Nordy's enough to know that before noon in the middle of the week the place is like a mausoleum.

I found a spot with a view of where he'd come in. The Nordstrom ground floor has an entry to the main parking lot, and the store has these comfortable chairs in different places, so an hour before he was due, I grabbed one, took out my phone and did the finger thing like I'm browsing my Twitter pals or Instagram pics. It was blend-in time.

No one notices me. I'm a junior in high school and I can look good—well, at least okay—when I want to. But on this errand

I'm dressed down: skinny jeans, long-sleeve rash guard top, no makeup, brown hair in pigtails, so I look younger and frankly kind of effing drab. I'm no raving beauty, so not being noticed comes easy. A tall, regular girl just chillin'.

My black rash guard top is surfer wear. If a wave dumps you and you get rolled along the bottom, you don't get your skin all scuffed. It's a poly material, fits tight. A rash guard is a handy item of clothing if a person is falling down an escalator and tries to grab your arm. That certain person won't get a good grip or scratch you with his nails if you're wearing a rash guard like mine.

You probably won't find that tip on the label. LOL.

Sure enough, fifteen minutes before his appointment, he comes bouncing through the glass doors, bouncing as much as a tubby old fart like him can bounce. He's like fifty or so. Hard to tell with old guys. He's dressed to impress: that's probably his best suit, a pinstripe number, white shirt and tie. He looks like a bag of potatoes.

I know where and when he's going to show up because Charlotte called him yesterday and told him about the thousand dollar sports jacket he'd won in the drawing.

We had him on speakerphone.

"I didn't enter any drawing," he said. I'm laughing to myself. *Of course you didn't, Mr. Brainiac.*

Charlotte put on her adult voice and read the script.

"Yessir, that may be the case. But someone put your business card in the bowl, and the department manager drew it out this morning. So congratulations. Can you come in for a fitting at 11:45 tomorrow?"

He bounces through the doors, heading for the up escalator, thinking he's won a jacket that retails for a thousand bucka-rooskies.

I tap a message to Charlotte, letting her know the creep is in the store. Now she'll move to what I call Phase 2 and she insists is

Phase II, pronounced eye-eye, because she's that kind of person with that sense of humor. Where I'm plain, Char is a classic beauty. Where I'm angling for an athletic scholarship, Char plans to be an actress. She's borrowed a sheath dress from her mom and gone all the way with eyeliner, pearl earrings and necklace. I look about fourteen and Char could pass for twenty-three.

When the guy comes in I think wheee! He's here! I get a prickly feeling. My stomach flips. It's the adrenaline. I've felt it plenty of times before tournaments and meets.

A stray thought: Am I really going to kill this dork?

The answer comes back: It's time for him to go. I flash on what MM told us about her seven-year-old sister, Emma, and this guy, the stepfather, slinking into the kid's room at bedtime.

I tamp it down, keep the cool in place, meander along behind Tubby. I take my time. I know what's gonna happen. He'll go up the escalator and make the U-turn to the men's department. With a smile on his face, he says he's here for his big prize, the thousand dollar sports jacket. The salesguy will give him a gigantic blank look, and will go find the manager because, after all, the servants aren't always in the loop. The manager will come out and explain to Tubby that there *isn't* any drawing, there never *was* any drawing, there will never *be* a drawing. My guess is the manager will say all this in the sort of way that will let Tubby know that Nordstrom is different from Pinstripes-R-Us where Tubby got the econo number he's wearing.

In short, Tubby will be made to feel like the fool he is, which the manager will probably be pretty good at getting across.

Char and I talked this over: At this point Tubby will be royally steamed. He will have little puffs smoke coming out of his ears. His eyes will be rolled back in his head and turned red. He will only be able to think about how he's been shown up as a total and complete dunce in front of the manager and whoever else was standing there staring at him.

No, he won't be browsing the ties and belts. He'll be walking fast, tromping back to the down escalator. He'll make the tight U-turn to get on, and...

Uh-oh! Someone not paying attention when they get on a down escalator! That's when accidents will happen!

I trail along behind Tubby on his way up to the men's department, and I'm saying to myself, hey, kiddo, time to step on the cockroach who preys on the small and the weak.

This adventure has a nice scary feel to it. A rollercoaster at that moment before the first drop.

It's funny, in a way, because the decision to kill him just popped out.

It started when Char and I heard MM sobbing in a stall of the girl's bathroom at school. Her name is Mary but Char started calling her Mary Mary in the third grade, probably from Mary Mary Quite Contrary. She wasn't contrary at all, Char just started calling her that, who knows why. So of course I picked it up. Then another Mary showed up at school so *everyone* started calling her Mary Mary, and then it got shortened to MM.

We calmed her down and got the story: her step father was copping feels, saying things, hitting on her when her mom wasn't around. That was one thing. MM told him to keep his dirty effing hands to himself. Then MM's little sister, Emma, told her the creep was coming into Emma's room at bedtime, talking about the stuff she might get for Christmas, which was eight months away. If you know anything about molesters, that's called grooming. He was putting his hands under the covers. Emma felt weird and told her big sister.

MM went to her mom.

Her mom didn't want to hear it. Mom said MM was asking for it, wearing leggings, sticking her butt out. As for Emma, mom said she was always in a tizzy over nothing.

Stepdad was the breadwinner and so on and so forth, and at her age, mom wasn't going to find another guy like him, blah

blah blah. So she wasn't gonna rock the boat. And besides, MM had it wrong, he wasn't like that. He wasn't that kind of person.

Yeah, like no one's ever heard that before.

But MM's mom did say something to him and stepdad got mad and MM saw the change in him. He started pressing and she could see where things were headed.

By this time our conversation had moved to a table in the far corner of the library where we squeezed together and talked in whispers. MM sat between us. I was propped with my elbow on the table, MM slouched down between us.

We went over it from every angle: what can we do about this pedo? We were going around and around when it popped out of my mouth: "He needs to have an accident."

MM was staring at her hands in her lap. She goes, "Yeah, an accident where his dick falls off."

But Char and I had a look going on over her head. Char read my face and I read hers. Nothing more needed to be said. We knew it right then. Time for him to go.

I watch Tubby bounce to the up escalator.

I take my time following along to the second floor. I check it out. Almost empty, as expected.

The cosmetics counter is the closest one to the down escalator, and Char is there at the far end where the perfumes are, picking up bottles of Chanel. She's dressed to kill—hey, wasn't that a movie from the olden days?—she beckons the salesgirl over.

I have a choice of seating. There's a pair of the super nice grey chairs facing back toward the men's department, and another pair tucked right beside the down escalator.

I really do love this store!

I grab one of the chairs facing the men's department.

Now the timing is important.

I hold my cell at eye level so it doesn't look like I'm spying.

They're at the far end of the men's department with counters and clothing racks in the way, so I can only get glimpses. After a couple minutes I see the manager come out from somewhere and I know it won't be long.

Either this will work or it won't. Maybe Tubby will decide to look at other stuff. Maybe someone he knows will show up and they'll hang together. Maybe he won't use the down escalator at all, maybe he'll wander out into the mall, head for the Little Miss Dress Shop to see if there are any naked mannequins in the window.

We think we have it figured, but like in baseball and wall quoits, you never know.

And then I spot him heading my way, walking fast. I feel the rush in my arms and legs that tunes me up.

I jump up and scoot over to one of the chairs next to the down escalator, looking over to see that Char is at Skin Care, using a brush on her cheeks, comparing Skin Foundation SPF 15 to Intensive Skin Serum Foundation SPF 40, acting like she's looking in a mirror but really spotting that I've moved to the Ready Zone.

Here's the plan: She makes a mess on the counter, opens samples, spills powder, drops brushes. When she leaves the counter to get on the escalator behind me, covering my moves, the salesgirl is busy cleaning up the mess, never looks over at the escalator.

From the chair next to the escalator, I do a final sweep. The place is like Antarctica. Let me tell you, if you're going to pop a cap on a guy at Nordstrom, just before noon on a Wednesday is a good time to do it.

Take the shoe department in front of me. As expected, the girl and guy working there, who are into each other, are huddled at the sales desk all the way at the far wall. No reason for them to pay any attention to anyone getting on the escalator.

And here he comes, stepping along. He looks grim. Yes, he's pissed.

Just as he passes me I'm up and close behind him, centered on his body, matching every roll and sway, adjusting my position to be right where I need to be. This is stuff Char and I worked on for hours after school using a mat in the gym, how he would walk and move and how I would control his posture, use his momentum against him.

He makes the tight U-turn, steps onto the down escalator with his right foot, and I'm there, my Converse hard on top of his trailing shoe and for me everything shifts into s-l-o-w motion.

But for him it's

MY GOD WHAT'S HAPPENING?

His weight isn't coming forward like it's supposed to and

JESUS! I'M GONNA FALL!

All my moves are planned, choreographed.

He swings his left arm out to grab the handrail and I'm turbocharged. It's like spotting a girl in gymnastics, which I've been doing since I was eight. Say she's practicing a dismount from the balance beam. You're there to help her turn or not turn, help her get safely onto the mat.

Same thing with Tubby.

I bring my right hand across and grab his left forearm, jerking him off the handrail. At the same time my left arm goes around his rib cage and I grab a handful of pinstripe as far as I can reach. My left foot is planted on a step and I'm travelling with him. He's got hold of nothing and I've got leverage. His brain is getting an emergency message:

IT'S ALL WRONG!

And he stiffens, which doesn't help him but is great for me. I turn him as he's falling and I can tell when he figures out it's going to be bad:

The breath comes out of him in a low moan.

When he's face up and about to hit, I plant a foot it in his chest and jump with all my weight. He smacks hard on his back then his head whips down and hits with a crunchy chunk that sounds like breaking stalks of celery. Sooo satisfying!

All the way down Charlotte's been close behind me, blocking the view of anyone who might notice.

At the bottom, the escalator slides us off and Tubby's head lolls, nice and loose.

Char scrambles to the side and says real loud, "This girl tried to keep him from falling!" Just in case anyone's wondering.

As people on the ground floor start to move toward us, Charlotte and I ease back. Everyone's gawking at Tubby and no one notices as two girls meander away and stroll through the store and out into the mall where they catch the elevator up to the Food Court.

That's right, the Food Court. Coming down from all that adrenaline gives you a terrible thirst.

We're quiet till we get drinks and food and a table at the back. Then Charlotte goes, "What do you think?"

I go, "Sounded to me like the poor guy broke his neck. Maybe he's a goner or a paraplegic or something."

"Too bad," she says.

"Yeah," I say, "I'm so, so sorry."

We exchange a smile: *as if.*

"You know," Charlotte says, "you're really a vicious little bitch."

We're sitting there in the Food Court and honest to God, it's all I can do to keep from spewing Diet Pepsi out of my nose.

Writing as a Teenage girl in "Sorry"

This is another story that was written for a contest, this one sponsored by the Crime Writers group at Scribophile. I didn't have any plans to enter the contest, and then one day I was in Nordstrom, and there it was, the escalator.

If I was at all successful in catching the rhythms and tone of a teenage girl, it's probably because I watched my daughter, Emily, grow up.

The story was published in January 2020 in *Fabula Argentea Magazine* (Latin for silver story), "the venue of good writing," as it says on the masthead. The photo that the editor, Rick Taubold, used to illustrate the story is one I took of the very elevator where I pictured the crime taking place.

About halfway through the writing, I was worried about how to end it because I didn't have an ending in mind. Then I decided to do something that Robert B. Parker does in so many of his novels—make a joke. Readers like jokes. Mine isn't great, but it worked well enough to get an editor to go for it.

After the story was finished and published, I learned something about writing fiction from it.

The most difficult part of the story to write was the justification for the crime. It had to be passionately motivated. The girls have to make the decision to do it in a way that is plausible for the reader. So I knew I had to write a scene with another high school girl in it, but I didn't want to get into all the ho-hum, introduce the character, explain the situation sort of stuff.

So I made up the tall tale about MM's name, the evolution of her nickname by Charlotte, and then at school. I started it in the girl's bathroom, and then moved it to the library in an attempt to give it a bit more presence, make it real, create a "yeah, that's what they would do" feeling in the reader.

When I got that section finished, I felt quite pleased with myself. I thought I had dreamed up a magic trick. Look over here! This is a little animated vignette! But what's really going on is the inciting incident for the entire story, though I never thought of the phrase "inciting incident" as I was writing it.

Is there some rule that says the inciting incident has to be at the beginning of the story?

It was only much later that I realized that I hadn't done a magic trick at all. What I had done by accident was stumble onto a feeling that is universal and powerful. It's this: Childhood friends can provide a powerful motivating force. It's not the cute stuff about the nickname at all that makes the scene work, it's the fact they had been friends since the third grade. Think about it, the kids we knew when we were in high school and younger, there's a particular and significant bond there that lasts a lifetime, even if you don't see them for years. So if your character interacts with a friend from childhood, your reader will accept a strong sense of loyalty between the two. It's so simple and such common sense, but I didn't see it until I stubbed my toe on what I'd done.

For me, learning to write has always seemed like a continuing process of ever increasing awareness of the sorts of images and emotions that trigger receptivity in the reader.

Suspense and Forwards

Fifteen years ago or so I realized that I had no idea how to write a story with suspense, or even what the hell it was. What is suspense? It's like one of those questions that came up around a table at the Art Canteen when we were undergrads: "What's the different between morals and ethics?"

So I did what I've often done when there's something I know I don't know, I looked into it.

I read what I could find about Alfred Hitchcock, the *master of suspense* as they say. I paid a lot of attention to the example of two people having lunch in a restaurant—no suspense. Then you show a ticking bomb under the table. Now you've got suspense. This isn't really helpful when you're looking at a blank page trying to figure out how to write a story that contains suspense but there aren't two people having lunch with a ticking bomb under the table. I wasn't looking for examples, I could find those for myself. I wanted the principles, the mechanics of how suspense worked, and it seemed to be something nobody knew.

Though interesting, nothing anyone said about Alfred Hitchcock and suspense gave me any hints about how to write suspense into my stories, or (perhaps better) how to write stories that were suspenseful.

Then I found Ken Follett's lecture at the 92nd Street Y, titled, *The Art of Suspense*. It's probably still on the internet.

Ahh, I thought, this will tell me what I want to know. Unfortunately, though interesting, his talk is about the history of thrillers. He's erudite and congenial but had nothing to say that was of practical help. The best line from the lecture is what Follett reports his agent said of a first draft of a novel: "You've written a tapestry, and what you need is a series of linked melodramas."

When I go on one of these research expeditions, I simply follow my nose. I don't remember how I found it, but eventually I stumbled across a book called *Backwards & Forwards, a Technical Manual for Reading Plays* by David Ball, Southern Illinois University Press, 1983, used with permission. This slender book of about 100 pages contains the essence of suspense and shows how to get it into your writing.

There's a good deal of interesting information in the book about plays and writing them that applies equally to stories and novels, but the core thing I was looking for I found beginning on page 45, in the chapter called *Forwards: Hungry for Next*. (The phrase hungry for next is a pretty good definition of suspense. When you've got the reader hungry for next, you've got suspense going on.)

Here's two quotes from the book, reprinted with permission:

A forward is anything that arouses an audience's interest in things yet to come.

And this:

The playwright must seize control of audience attention... Thus, skilled playwrights load scenes with forwards, so no matter how

strong the scene (or weak) the audience is maneuvered into an eager-
ness to remain to see what's next.

That's what you want from that opening to your novel, huh? There's a great example of a first paragraph of genre fiction that is loaded with forwards, James Sallis' novel *Drive*. You can read the first paragraph using the Look Inside feature on Amazon. Notice the opening words: *much later*, that's a forward. If a character watches a puddle of blood seep toward him, that's a forward; if the character second guesses himself about what he's done, that's a forward; if the sun is coming up and people are starting to be out and about and you're sitting with your back against a wall and everything around you reeks of crime scene, that's a forward.

Easily passed over phrases *much later* and *later still*, are essential forwards, since they cue the reader to an awareness of a future in which some interesting stuff is going to go on.

I don't want to dwell on genre fiction, though. There are as many ways to do it as there are writers with stories to tell. The opening of *Then We Came to the End*, a novel by Joshua Ferris sounds like one long forward. Filled with contradictions and bereft of explanation, the paragraph raises the question, who are these people and what the hell is going on? You can also find the opening paragraphs to this novel using the Look Inside feature on Amazon.

Is it a coincidence that both of those first two examples lack explanations? Not at all.

My last example is in the literary genre, so it's slower at the beginning and takes a bit longer to develop, but it's worth a read. *A Little Life* by Hana Yanagihara includes an interesting first sentence with a sort of awkward "smoking" tacked on at the end. There are more polished ways to get the smoking into the sentence, but Ms. Yanagihara didn't choose one of them. And it's not because she didn't notice it or lacked the skill to deal with it.

Makes me go hmm. The hook in this opening occurs when the real estate agent tells Jude and Willem they can't rent the apartment because they don't make enough money or have any savings. Then she wonders about these two guys in their twenties who aren't a couple renting a one-bedroom apartment. It makes the reader wonder the same thing.

Drive is for one sort of reader, *Then We Came to the End* and *A Little Life* are for a different, perhaps smaller subset of readers, though I understand *A Little Life* has sold over a million copies.

Making Sense of the Five Senses

A colleague recently started a thread asking about what senses a writer should and shouldn't use, and pointed out that there are more than five senses. As a matter of fact, my colleague said that on the internet it's easy to find scientific papers describing up to 33 senses.

Here's an example of a writer trying to use physical senses to get across what her character is feeling:

Susan Jones raced down the sidewalk throwing glances over her shoulder. He was closing in on her. Her heart thudded wildly; each breath was a struggle, her aching chest felt ready to explode.

I've seen this sort of description fairly often, and it seems to me that it's based on the idea that giving the reader a lot of sense information about the character is how one gets the reader to understand how the character feels—if I tell you the physical sensations the character is experiencing, you, the reader, will feel that way too.

My intuition told me it doesn't work that way, but I was never able to formulate why. Now I think I may have figured it out, which I think is contrary to advice one sometimes sees.

In the interests of scholarship and research, allow me to quote how Claire North handled the opening in her wonderful novel *Touch* using only 50 words and no physical sensations:

> *Josephine Cebula was dying, and it should have been me.*
>
> *She had two bullets in the chest, one in the leg, and that should have been the end of it, should have been enough, but the gunman had stepped over her expiring form and was looking for me.*
>
> *For me.*

I think the key thing to understand from the first example above with Susan Jones is that the writer can't make the reader feel excitement by describing sense information. I think the optimum approach is to try to give the reader an understanding of what's going on, like Claire North does, and make sure that understanding will include dramatic tension, by which I mean feelings of *anticipation* and *uncertainty*.

In the *Touch* example, the protagonist's only emotion is indignant surprise in the phrase *For me*. Claire North doesn't even bother with an exclamation point. It's up to the reader to read into how that phrase gets expressed and what it means, which we can't help doing. (Well, there's the protagonist's feeling in the first sentence too. But the emotion is expressed through the situation, not by saying how she felt.)

I think there is a guiding idea here for fiction writing: emotion on the part of the reader comes from situation, not from having a character describe how it feels.

So how do we translate this theory into an example. Here's a revision of the Susan Jones episode mentioned above:

> *Arms and legs powered by pure fear, pumping faster than they'd ever done on the high school track team, Susan Jones sprinted down the*

midnight sidewalk. Thank God she'd kicked off her shoes when she started running, she could never have gotten away from him in high heels. When she glanced back, she could see his dark form, and the glint a streetlight made on the blade of the knife he held aloft. He was closing on her. Susan knew if he caught her she was as good as dead. But what scared her most was what he would do to her before he slit her throat.

What physical sensations is Susan Jones experiencing? Sure, she's breathless, panting, getting tired, and on and on for all 33 possible senses, if you want to get into it. But the reader doesn't want all that, because the reader's neurons are firing plenty of information along the lines of how-would-I-feel-if-that-happened-to-me. No, your reader has probably never been chased down the street by a madman with a knife, but she's seen plenty of TV shows and movies, and she's got a vivid imagination.

5

Whence We Came, Whither We Go

WHEN THE DRUNK IN THE OVERNIGHT tank starts in with the DTs screaming about bugs crawling up his arms, you can hear it all over the jail, and let me tell you, after a while it grinds on your nerves. So finally after an hour or so of the yelling, the sheriff tells me take him over to emergency at the hospital.

"Let them deal with that sorry son-of-a-gun," says the sheriff, a tough old bird everyone calls Buster. The drunk with the DTs is a repeat occupant of the tank, a once-in-a-while farmhand named Nowak. I'm a deputy sheriff with a name badge says Teja.

At the emergency room, a couple fellows help get Nowak out of the back of the patrol car and manhandle him up onto a gurney where they strap him down. I follow them into emergency where they take him to a treatment room that has curtains for walls. Nowak is still yelling, and I'm holding onto the gurney that Nowak is making rock back and forth despite the straps. So with all the noise, it doesn't take long for a doctor and nurse to come in. They recognize Nowak, the doctor is calling him Julius and trying to calm him down and the nurse turns to me and tells me to hold his arm so it doesn't move. I grab hold of Nowak and the nurse sticks him with a needle and that's all she wrote—it's like dropping a rock. Nowak goes from wacky as a fruitcake to unconscious in about ten seconds. I unlock the cuffs and the nurse straps his wrists to the bed rails. She's in her forties, some gray hair, no wasted motion. Everything about her says been there done that.

The doc leaves and it's just me and her in this cubicle with curtains, kind of private. I can tell she's about to leave too, so I give it a shot.

"Could I ask you something?" I say. I got this buddy, I tell her —it comes rolling out of me—back from Afghanistan six months, cries a lot on the weekends. Weekdays he's okay, but weekends he can't stop the tears. What does she think about that?

She gives me a look, like up to now she hasn't noticed I was there.

"Yeah," she says, "PTSD. He should have his primary care physician refer him to a psychologist." She brushes the curtain open and she's gone.

Well hell, I think, that didn't work for sour owl shit.

I took a discharge after my second tour with Operation Enduring Freedom. Back in civvies, I caught on with the sheriffs. It's an easy transition from the military. You've got a uniform, you've got a weapon, you've got a chain of command and standard operating procedures. You follow orders, keep your head down, your mouth shut, do the job and it works just fine.

Wednesday through Sunday, work days, things are good. But Mondays and Tuesdays, my days off, alone in a furnished studio, I cry. I'm okay if I need to go somewhere, pick up laundry, hit the grocery store. But when I'm alone the tears just keep coming. I tell myself It's the Afghan crud and it will run its course. But it doesn't.

It's not something I want to tell anyone about. Hell, I'm a deputy sheriff carries a gun on his hip. If I start to let it out I know I won't be able to keep the tears from coming. Even the little I told the nurse at the hospital, it was all I could do to keep from bending down and laying my head on her shoulder.

I thought the job would give me what I needed. Structure and discipline, those will set me right, I said to myself, just what law enforcement has to offer.

Buster, a rawboned old coot, balding, the other side of fifty, has a saddle leather face—rolled up tight and put away wet, as they say. When I was hired I naturally had a lot of respect for him. The commanding officer. Over the months, though, I watched his toughness spill over into a sort of peevishness, and sometimes go too far. Like the deal with Thatcher.

Thatcher is a skinny, long-haired kid, twenty years old, tattoos up and down his arms. We book him on fourth degree arson, which is as Mickey Mouse as it sounds, basically a campfire. I'm in the office when they bring him in, mouthing off about his civil rights. He has a chrome safety pin in his eyebrow.

The next day when the municipal court judge turns him loose on his own recognizance, Thatcher isn't a brash kid anymore. Head down, shoulders hunched, bruises on his arms and a bandage on his forehead—a little bloodstain where the safety pin used to be—he's a dog that's been whipped. Nobody in the office says anything. Buster is downright cheerful.

Especially on days when he feels good, Buster likes to get a few of us in his office, his boots up on his desk, directing traffic with the straw from his Doctor Pepper, and spout off.

"You know what they do in Singapore?" One of Buster's favorites is law enforcement in Singapore. "In Singapore they cane 'em. And once they've been caned, you better believe it, they straighten up and fly right. You chew gum, you get caned!"

I'm the only one on the force who's ever seen a caning. It's in a mud-brick village a few klicks outside Mazar-i-Sharif in Balkh province. The tribal council, a dozen men with beards and embroidered robes, sit cross-legged on rugs. In the middle of the room a boy is tied by his wrists to a post. He's maybe ten, naked from the waist down. They caught him with stuff he pilfered from our forward observation post and invited a few of us down the hill to see justice done. I was the ranking NCO.

The mullah, sleeves pushed up, hits the kid with the stick I'd seen them use to move their cattle. It's what our cattlemen hereabouts call a persuader, whippy, about four feet long, as big around as your thumb.

At first the kid screams. After about ten he doesn't have any scream left in him, only jumps and whimpers with each stoke. His skin is broken, blood trickles down his legs.

After a while the mullah comes over and hands me the stick. My interpreter says I'm required to give the final blow to show that we're satisfied.

I say no thanks. The interpreter insists—we have to keep the respect of the village. The interpreter says no holding back. The strength of my stroke has to show the strength of the soldiers manning the FOB.

That's where my mind goes when Buster starts in about what a great law enforcement tool we're missing out on because we don't have caning.

A week after Thatcher is set loose, the sheriff grabs my arm and tells me to drive out to the state line and meet up with the deputy from the neighboring state who's bringing a prisoner for transfer.

"They've picked up that kid Thatcher," the sheriff says. "Go get him and bring him in."

We transfer prisoners back and forth from time to time at a spot ninety miles out where the two-lane blacktop of our state becomes the two-lane blacktop of their state. It's a wide spot with a little bit of turnout and two green signs with white letters, one on each side of the highway. A sign that reads Now Entering on one side of the highway for their state, and one that says Now Entering on the other side of the road for ours.

When I get there I pull across the highway to the wrong side, putting my front bumper up against the other deputy's car.

He's a guy named Ray I've met a few times.

Ray opens the back door of his car and Thatcher spills out, stumbles on the shoulder then takes off running as fast as he can out across the high desert. He's wearing the same dirty T-shirt, shorts and sneakers, no socks, he wore the last time I saw him. His wrists are cuffed behind him so he's running hunched over.

It's so completely surprising and stupid, the hopelessness in this particular situation, trying to make a break for it like that, Ray and I just start to laugh, watching Thatcher scramble off across the desert where there absolutely isn't anywhere to go.

When our laughing dies out, Ray asks, "What do you think he has in mind?" and it starts us up again. There's nothing in that direction but eighty or ninety miles of chaparral, greasewood and manzanita.

Ray and I don't bother moving, just watch, our butts against the fenders of our cars, as Thatcher, a few hundred yards out and walking now since nobody is coming after him, disappears into a dip in the land.

Ray kicks the heel of his boot against the front tire of his car. "Well, I guess I'll head back."

"You ain't gonna help me go get him?"

"We don't want him. We picked him up as a vagrant. He's yours for the taking."

"He's wearing your cuffs."

"They put them on at the jail. I don't think they'll ask for them back."

Ray opens the door to his car, tosses me a *"Que tenga buen dia,"* spins a U-turn and speeds away.

I watch the spot where Thatcher disappeared. A breeze comes up. It's a lovely day, no other word for it. A few stratocumulus puffs on their way east across a whole lot of blue.

Have a good day, Ray said. There were a lot of days just like this in Afghanistan, the same sunlight, a breeze, a great long reach of brown land with far-off mountains grey and flat against the sky.

A group of villagers, maybe half a dozen, came trudging up the hill to our FOB. The mullah had the boy in his arms, wrapped in a blanket. Our medic, Holcomb, lifts the flap of the olive drab tent with the red cross on it. Holcomb has patched up villagers before, and their faces are hopeful as the mullah puts the boy on the table.

Holcomb folds back the blanket. The boy is mottled, stiff, and cold. His eyes are closed and his face... How to say it? It's at rest. He's beautiful. He was a beautiful boy. Holcomb says, "I'm sorry," and lets his arms drop to his sides. There's no need for translation. They burst into cries and wails, the women weeping.

A place so far away, I had no idea who I was or what I was doing—a soldier who held life and death at port arms with one in the chamber, a person who could wave a hand at the radio operator and summon death from the sky.

Who was I, that I could hit a child as hard as I did? Who was I that could do such a thing?

Me and the nitwit Thatcher waiting it out on a stretch of land not that much different from where I'd been. Thatcher, that poor pathetic jerk. Too young and too dumb to understand that there were people in the world like Buster and me. Yes, me and Buster, we had a couple things in common. Maybe the only difference is I'm a crybaby about it.

I run a hand through my hair, my stomach grumbles and I look at my watch. Ten past one. There's a diner a few miles back, but I can wait. I'm good at waiting.

It takes an hour before Thatcher comes walking back across the desert, about as bedraggled and hopeless as it's possible to be. He's peed himself and there are streaks down his cheeks where he's been crying. When I take the cuffs off him, I can see where he's scraped the skin on his wrists, probably against a rock trying to get the cuffs off. He's got a good-sized scab on his eyebrow.

I take the service blanket out of the trunk of the car to wrap around him and drive the two of us to the diner for matching cheeseburgers and fries, finished off with apple pie and coffee for me, soda pop for Thatcher. I find out everything about him I need to know. He is a dumb kid, but hell, we were all dumb kids once, weren't we?

After lunch we drive into town and I take him to Walmart and buy him a pair of jeans, a T- shirt and underwear. His old clothes go in a trash bin. Then I take him to the Greyhound station and buy him a ticket to Portland where his parents live. I give him two twenties and watch the bus pull out.

It was so wrong, so many moving parts, no one thing could have made it right, could have changed what happened. Was that true or just something I needed to tell myself to help me feel better? Was it all foretold, set up to happen so it had to happen? Was it possible to stick a dumb kid on a bus and make things turn out different somewhere down the line?

I stood there and admired the exhaust from the Greyhound's diesel, the way the blue-grey smoke hung in a shadow, drifting, taking its own sweet time about deciding where to go and what to do when it got there.

My Interlude with PTSD and "Whence"

Where do stories come from? I mean in the mind of the writer, what gets them going?

I don't know about anyone else, but for me they start when something drops into focus in my mind. That's what it feels like. I've written an exaggerated version of the feeling in the last story in this book, *Death Leap*, where the character Christine is struck with the idea for a reality television show. I exaggerated for the story, but for me that's sort what it's like, in cartoon-speak, the lightbulb goes on.

The image that started this one came to me when I was scrolling through some thread or other at the online writing site Scribophile. It was a vivid picture in my mind of the place out on a lonely two-lane highway where a prisoner exchange might take place. The prisoner tries to run, and the deputy sheriff watches him go, knowing there isn't any place to run to. It was the notion of the futility of it all that got my motor running, and though some readers might think that is the inciting incident in the story, it doesn't seem entirely that way to me. For me, there are a series of incidents in the story, some in real time, some remembered, that come together into Teja's story that makes it happen. So maybe there doesn't have to be one inciting incident, maybe a series of incidents can make a story happen. Or maybe the incident is a war in a far-off country.

Because of this phrase in the story, "*Que tenga buen dia*," readers assume Teja is Hispanic. Truth is I borrowed the name from a good Army buddy, Gur Dave Teja (1934-2010), whose parents emigrated from India. Dave was raised on an almond ranch near Yuba City, California. The Teja in the story only shares a name with Dave Teja the person. Dave and I were stationed on Pepperrell Air Force Base just outside St. John's, Newfoundland as part of the U.S. Army Transportation Terminal Command Arctic. Almost every evening, after dinner, I would cajole Dave into a few games of pocket billiards in the rec room in the basement of the barracks. This was before Dave's wife joined him and they rented an apartment in St. John's that became a hangout for the guys that included Arnold Shimazu, the perfect soldier from Hawaii, and Don LePeau from Massachusetts who had a VW bug. During that long, cold winter in Newfoundland, a homesick Arnold would try to talk us into going outside, digging a pit, lining it with stones, lighting a fire and cooking a fish. "No Arnold," we would say, "we're going down to the mess hall."

I spent a while on Google Maps looking for an actual place an incident like Thatcher trying to run away may have occurred, the borders of Texas and New Mexico, Arizona and Nevada, all around the West. There isn't any such place that comes close to matching what I had in mind, and I knew exactly what it looked like. So I invented the location I needed for the story. Everyone has seen so many movies and TV shows in settings like this, that my location is entirely credible.

The beginning was simply a matter of assembling the parts: I started the story in the jail the way I did so I could get Teja to the hospital where he could describe his problem to the nurse. That was problem 1 in the story, getting Teja's problem established. Then I brought in Thatcher because I had to get the prisoner in the story. Thatcher is vaguely modeled on a story a wacko kid told in a Synanon game: he was driving down a freeway about 2 a.m. when he ran out of gas. The car had just enough momentum to get halfway up an off ramp. The kid, who was on something at the time, in addition to being more than somewhat addled, was afraid that if he turned on the car's flashing warning lights they would drain the battery and soon go out. So he set the car on fire. Yes, sometimes Synanon games were hilarious.

The story Teja tells about caning the kid in the Afghan village I made up out of whole cloth. I found the account of the dead child posted by a physician on Twitter who was devastated by it. I couldn't improve on his report: *mottled, stiff, and cold*. That description was the impetus for that whole sequence in the story, everything that led up to it.

The PTSD in the story occurred in 1966, when I came back to the States after six months working as a civilian in Saigon during the Vietnam War.

Earlier in the 1960s I'd done a one-year overseas contract on Johnston Island in the Central Pacific, a thousand miles the other side of Hawaii, and while there had worked for the engineers who wrote out the specs for construction bills of materials in the office where I typed them up.

A couple years later, I was working for a small trade magazine publishing company in Los Altos, California, writing about two-thirds of two quarterly magazines, *New Homes Guide* and *Home Modernizing Guide*, when I got a phone call from one of the Johnston Island engineers I'd known. He was processing through San Bruno, just up the San Francisco Peninsula, and needed a place to stay for a couple days while he was in transit. I said sure. He asked me if I would like a job in Vietnam. At the time I was making $400 a month. The Vietnam job paid $1,500 a month, which was tax free if you stayed for one year. My buddy said he would put in a name requisition for me. I didn't believe it would happen, but about three months later I got a call from San Bruno: "How would you like to go to Vietnam?"

I stayed six months. When I came back, like Teja in the story, I couldn't stop crying. I didn't know what was wrong with me, though I think I did come to an understanding of it later when I got some perspective. But all I wanted then was to make it go away. I made an appointment with a Beverly Hills psychiatrist, a beautiful office, matching upholstered wingback chairs, he in one, me in another. A handsome man, graying hair, beautifully turned out in a light gray suit and yellow knit tie. At the end of my recitation of history and symptoms, he said, "I think I can work with you."

That's it? I thought. A hundred and twenty-five bucks and I think I can work with you?

In Los Angeles at this time, the founder of Synanon, the drug rehab place in Santa Monica, had been thrown into jail on what he called a zoning rap. The organization was all over the news. I went out to visit during open house on a Sunday afternoon, and spent a couple hours drinking coffee with a Black kid from Philadelphia who recounted his history of drug abuse, what was called in Synanon-speak his dirty rotten story. Newcomers were encouraged to run their dirty rotten stories, it was part of the process of coming to terms with who they had been, as contrasted to who they wanted to become.

The following week, I was sitting in a circle of twelve people playing the Synanon Game. Toward the end of the session, they asked me who I was. I told them a couple things, and then a skinny kid, I found out later was a newcomer, he'd been in Synanon three months or so, leaned forward in his chair and said, "I'll tell you what your problem is, you're a pathological liar." Someone else said, "That's a projection!" and another person added, "Yes, but projections are valid!" The Synanon Games were a lot of fun and my mild case of PTSD disappeared.

For the first three months this story was being revised, the title was *The Empty Place*. Then, for some unknown reason (well actually prospecting for who knows what), I was reading the *George Sand—Gustave Flaubert Letters*, which are in the public domain. In her letter to Flaubert of 28 September, 1866, George Sand wrote:

> *I dream so much and I live so little, that sometimes I am only three years old. But, the next day I am three hundred, if the dream has been somber. Isn't it the same with you? Doesn't it seem at moments, that you are beginning life without even knowing what it is, and at other times don't you feel over you the weight of several thousand centuries, of which you have a vague remembrance and a sorrowful impression? Whence do we come and whither do we go? All is possible since all is unknown.*

There was the title. With that new title, came a change in focus for the story, and with the encouragement of several of my colleagues (*First, I would absolutely delete the first two paragraphs*, Ross Murdock hinted gently) came a new beginning, and buoyed by their remarks about the ending (*not really satisfying* was as kind as anyone got), I didn't have an ending that worked, but I did have good directions in which to look from my colleague Guillermo Stitch, which, of course, isn't his real name.

The ending of the story arrived during one of the final revisions, beginning to end, for what turned out to be the last time. I got to the point where Teja gives him two twenties and puts him on the bus, and at that point the last two paragraphs, and especially the last paragraph, just came into my mind. Who knows from where?

Well, I do know from where, and so does anyone familiar with the epiphany at the ending 0f the James Joyce story *The Dead*. Joyce had the snow softly falling into the dark mutinous Shannon waves, and I have the exhaust fumes from a Greyhound bus.

Humiliation, Get Used to It

If you are anything like me, and you probably are, our problems with writing fiction (or inadequacies or faults or difficulties—call them what you will) are probably in large measure a result of our natural inclinations.

Don't feel special, we all have our tendencies, the way we were born, were raised, grew up, were educated, experiences. All these things (but probably mostly the way we were born) influence how we are in the world. And how we are in the world determines what interests us and *what* we write and *how* we write it.

Here's what happens to me: someone points out something about my story in a critique, and I think, "How can I be so blind to this very obvious thing? Have I always been this stupid, this obtuse?"

The answer often is that (not surprisingly) what I've done in my story plays to my nature.

Are your natural inclinations toward ideas rather than toward people? Are your natural inclinations toward world-building and the conflict of ideologies and story events and not so much (or even at all about) the problems those events create for a character, and on the thoughts and feelings of a character?

Or are you the opposite: do your natural inclinations pull you strongly into a powerful empathy for the feelings of your character so that you're entirely comfortable relating these feelings and like to describe them at length?

When you first start getting crits on your work, (like for the first twenty years or so), it can feel like humiliation. After all, you've put your heart and soul into doing something very personal only to have some cruel, thoughtless s.o.b. point out how dumb you've been about this or that.

I don't think it's just me who has ever felt this way.

The humiliation I feel when I get a crit, that's my ego. That's my personal belief that I am (actually, despite what anyone might think) quite perfect, and so of course whatever it is I write is equally faultless.

But if you're going to write and let people read your stuff, you must push through this discomfort. It's not optional. The real choice is: do you want to stay where you are, or do you want to get better at it?

The test is this: Am I willing to accept the embarrassment and humiliation of making mistakes and get at the truth about my writing, or would I rather skip the truth and not be embarrassed about the dumb thing I wrote (though it's still something dumb and it's still something I wrote—and I assure you I've written a lot of dumb stuff)?

(And look at that terrible run-on sentence. But you know what I mean.)

Hemingway had a wonderful advantage over the rest of us. First he worked for newspapers and saw his stuff torn apart and put back together by the rewrite desk. Then he had editors who pointed out what was wrong. Then he went to Paris, where he had F. Scott Fitzgerald, James Joyce, Ford Maddox Ford, and

Gertrude Stein to read his stuff and tell him where he went wrong. And he still included plenty of clinkers.

It helps to have a few good readers. But you have to be willing to put up with what they say.

And then there's the learning curve. You'll post something, get feedback from four or five fellow writers, make every single change and revision they've suggested, and find as a result that somehow something essential that was there when you started has been made to vanish. You have to be a bit more discriminating.

On the one hand, all critiques are valid, and though they are valid for the person making them, that doesn't necessarily mean they're valid for what you've written. And sometimes the person offering the crit won't understand the true nature of their objection. It doesn't matter what you write, there will be those who don't care for it, who will be out of tune with it, who will be on a different wavelength.

But on the other hand, I hope you will find colleagues, such as I have, who are *simpatico* with what you're trying to do, who get it, and who can offer suggestions that will help you get to where you're trying to go.

6

The Call for Help

*There comes a time you don't get to shrug and walk away,
and this was one of them.*

WE WERE SETTING IN THE BACK of the general store, Carl Yazzie
up on the edge of his chair, his gut hanging over his belt, his
craggy face all lit up, right at the best part of the story, his hands
out to show where he'd been standing and where the Swedish
professor had been standing in the fishing camp when the bear
came out of the woods. We'd heard it a bunch of times. It was
uncommonly funny the way the bear come shambling out of the
woods and the Swedish professor shit his pants.

There's certain things you want to do and not do when a bear
shows up, and shitting your pants is pretty near the bottom of the
list, bears having a real good sense of smell and being of a
curious nature.

Right then the door banged and the kid came slamming into
the place with a rush of icy air, sneakers slapping the floor, skit-
tering across the planks back to where we was sitting. The general
store, a big old place built years ago, all raw timber, no windows,

and at the back where the hardware shelves end Old Jeff kept half dozen chairs and apple boxes circled up under a lightbulb, its cord looped over a cross beam.

Carl stopped telling his story as the boy skidded to a stop and looked around, catching his breath, his cheeks all rosy. He had on high-top sneakers, faded jeans, and a down vest over a blue T-shirt. It had been snowing in flurries all day and there were flecks in his hair.

The kid belonged to a man and his wife who'd showed up a year or so ago in this part of Alaska in a crew cab pickup truck pulling a travel trailer, which they set up on a couple acres on the edge of the village. Said they was putting up a broadcast radio station, which seemed a peculiar thing do way out here in the backcountry, so I said to myself, yeah sure, and never paid it much mind. The boy, Kenny, was one of the home-schooled kids always around; fourteen or so, skinny like they are at that age, sun-dark enough to pass for a native, with a haircut that looked like his ma did it when she noticed, which is the way it was for a lot of kids.

The kid took a couple deep breaths, gathering himself. I expected some yelling. What I got was a voice all level and calm. I remember exactly what he said:

"There's a man on the other side of the river calling for help."

We looked at him, not knowing if he might be playing a joke. Or maybe the *cheechako* kid had gone round the bend. In Alaska *cheechako* is what we call newcomers, it's from the Chinook language. The back country, the isolation, a couple hundred miles from the nearest traffic light, some folks can't handle it.

What the kid said had to be either a joke or the crazies, because there was no way on God's green earth and full spring thaw somebody could show up alive on the other side of the Copper River.

If you took a handful of toothpicks, the kind with points, and bundled them together in your fist and imagined the tips of them all white with snow, that was about what you saw when you flew over a lot of this country in winter, particularly to the north and east, the other side of the Copper.

The river started a hundred miles or so off in the mountains, fed from the Denali Range, the Talkeetnas and the Wrangells. At spring breakup who knows how many million acre-feet of snow and ice turned to water and came hurtling down through rock canyons in a wild plunge, going hell for leather to Valdez and the North Pacific.

There weren't no bridges across the Copper, and on the other side, it was pure emptiness and mountains. Anybody who tried to get to the Copper from that direction would be dead long before they made it.

So there wasn't one of us setting there who placed much credence in what young Kenny said.

Among our bunch of ne'er-do-wells—hunters, trappers, fishermen, guides, and general backcountry riff-raff, some of whom (including yours truly), would just as soon not have any official notice taken of them—was Hicky Johnson, a square-built, wide-shouldered commercial fisherman who went off in the summer to work one crab boat or another up in the Bering Sea. He wore his long grey-streaked hair in a ponytail.

Hicky was the one who most often spoke up first and loudest, as he did now.

"You're that Harper kid, ain't you?"

"I am." The kid's gaze was steady.

Hicky shifted and put his head at an angle.

"Well, if there is a man on the other side of the river calling for help, how do you think he got there?"

I could see the impatience come up in the way the kid started to jiggle.

"How the hell should I know how he got there?" he said. "You gonna do something or you just gonna sit there and ask me a bunch of dumb fucking questions?"

He didn't say it but I could hear it in the kid's voice: sit there on your big fat ass. Yeah, he wasn't fourteen at all. Maybe a good deal older, but built on the small side.

Hicky glared at the back-talk then come to his feet and took three big strides, his hand out to grab the kid, but by the time he got there the kid was halfway to the front door looking back to see if Hicky was following.

The door slammed as the kid went out and Hicky stood there looking after him. Then he said, "Dammit!" and headed for the row of nails where we hung our coats.

We trooped across the muddy road, a chill wind swirling snowflakes out of a grim sky, passed through a sparse stand of jack pine and come out onto the rounded river rock that slid and shifted underfoot as we made our way down to the water.

It was a long grey afternoon of on-and-off snow but visibility wasn't that bad. The river was about a hundred and fifty yards across.

We scanned the other bank and Burt Becenti said, "There's nary a thing over there."

The other side of the river was much the same as this side: twenty feet of river rock from water's edge back to a stand of pine.

"Burt, you're as blind as a fish worm in a coffee can," Tommy Nakai said. "See him there just to the right of that white rock?"

There was a fair-sized piece of granite, and just to the down-stream side of it, right at the water's edge, was a dark, longish shape.

"That's a driftwood log," Burt said, "got away from some prospector building a sluice or a shake table somewhere upstream."

"Nope," Tommy said, "it's a man all in black."

"The hell you say," Burt said.

About that time Old Jeff Oxendine showed up from the store and handed Hicky a pair of U.S. Navy surplus deck binoculars.

"Hold still," Hicky said to me and propped an elbow on my shoulder to steady the glasses as he peered across the river.

All doubt disappeared as the shape across the river raised an arm and waved it lazy-like back and forth.

"He's saying something," Hicky said, "I can see his mouth moving."

The river was thundering right along with a deep roar, pushing up standing waves that tumbled into foam as it came up against the boulders that studded the riverbed.

"I heard him," Dickie Bear said. He'd been standing off a bit from the rest of us.

"Well what did he say?" Morgan Chavis said.

"He said help," Dickie Bear replied. "What do you think he's gonna say, please pass the gravy?"

Hicky handed the binoculars to me. I could see a man in dark clothes, what looked like an oilcloth raincoat and the sort of wide-brim black hat a prospector might wear. It appeared he had a beard, though holding the binoculars without support, the image was shaky.

I passed the binoculars along and they went 'round amongst us.

As we took turns looking, Hicky said what I'd been thinking: "Ain't that a too-bad thing. Son-of-a-gun is stuck for sure."

"Gonna be cold tonight," Morgan Chavis put in, meaning it was going to go well below freezing, maybe down to zero, and it was no night to be laying beside a river in your raincoat.

Beyond that no one had much to say. We were all thinking the same: There was no way for that guy to get from that side of the river over to ours. The Copper was boiling along, a cataract angry as the devil and cold as death. From time to time chunks of ice the size of washtubs broke off upstream and careened along through the rapids, banging and knocking against boulders. Spend two minutes in that freezing water and your hands and arms are too cold to grab onto anything. Five minutes later, if you're still above water, you don't care anymore.

We stood there and watched, no one with anything much to say. I didn't want to be there, but there wasn't no way to get away from it. I wanted to say, hey, can't do no good here, let's go put on the coffeepot. I think the guys felt the same. But there comes a time you don't get to shrug and walk away and this was one of them.

It was downright unpleasant to spend a dull sunless twilight looking at a man across a river who's as good as dead.

Then Harper's big crew cab truck bounced through the trees, slewed across the river rock, turned sharp and come up short, the truck bed aimed at the river. In the back of the truck was an upside-down aluminum boat, one of those fourteen-footers like a lot of us have. Hanging tight with both hands to the bow rope of the boat, his feet braced against a tire well, was the Harper kid, Kenny.

Kenny's dad, Conrad, piled out of one door of the truck and Jason Goodwin came out the other. Right then my reckoning of Conrad Harper as a nutcase with a harebrained radio station idea underwent an on-the-spot alteration. Any man that Jason Goodwin took up with, well, that meant something.

Jason Goodwin ran the Standard Oil terminal in this end of the country, supplying folks with the stuff you need to survive, everything from gasoline to aviation fuel to arctic synthetic grease. When he wasn't doing that, he was hunting and fishing. He'd grown up in Alaska and there wasn't a whole lot he didn't know about the ways of this country.

They had that boat out of the bed of the truck and down to the water's edge in nothing flat. The outboard motor had been under the boat, and that was clamped to the stern in two minutes. A bundle wrapped in a tarp came out of the truck and went into the boat. All this with no more talking among the three of them than grab that, lift together, a little this way, and set her down easy.

The bow on the rocks, the stern in the water, Jason Goodwin stood beside the boat and gave the river a good look-see, a slow-moving thoughtful gaze. He was six-three or so, and lanky, in Levis and wool shirt. He kept his hair cut short and his whiskers at maybe a three-day growth.

The river was a churning torrent, breaking and spilling among the rounded boulders that dappled the streambed for five miles or more in either direction. It was melt water, milky in places, turquoise when the light caught it on account of the fine granite and quartz powder it held suspended. The sediment came from rocks grinding together underneath the mountain glaciers and the river smashing the rocks and rolling them along. There were standing waves where surges came up against outcrops, then deep eddies behind with sharp back currents.

We watched them put that boat in the water, and I think some of us were thinking what Hicky Johnson said: "Ain't no way you'll make it over and back."

Jason Goodwin said, "Think so, huh?"

Jason gave Hicky a bit of time to answer, and when he didn't, spoke again: "Ain't you got a boat leaning up against the back of your cabin over yonder?"

We all knew that Hicky did have a boat, and that his cabin was pretty close by.

I seen the color come up Hicky's neck into his cheeks.

He said, "You'll get swamped and capsize, or you'll shear a pin and that'll be the end of it."

With mention of the shear pin Hicky meant the steel pin, an inch long or so, that goes between the propeller and the drive-shaft of an outboard motor. It's set up so if the prop hits a rock, the pin shears in half to keep the driveshaft from getting bent. It's easy to fix a shear pin, but a drive shaft, that's a horse of another breed entirely. When the pin shears, the prop and the driveshaft are disconnected and the boat's got no power. You're finished going anywhere.

Jason took his time replying.

"Thanks for that, Hicky. I guess I should pay particular attention to not trying to drive through rocks, huh?"

At that Hicky seemed to shrink into himself.

I guess what Hicky didn't know is that anyone who runs a boat on the Copper, we take a welding torch to that shear pin feature and make sure it ain't ever going to shear no matter what the prop hits. Heck, that's just common sense. You don't want to be out there on that river flailing around like a goose with a busted wing.

Jason gave a couple instructions to Conrad and Kenny, then stepped into the boat and made his way to the stern. He tilted the outboard down so the prop was in the water and gave a pull to the starting rope. The motor caught on the first pull and Conrad Harper shoved the bow off the rocks, heading it upstream.

I'd never imagined it would come to somebody trying to take a boat across the Copper this time of year, so I'd never pictured how it might be done. But now that the boat was in the water, my first thought was that you'd want to rev that motor up and get the boat going up on top of the water so the hull ran as shallow as she could.

But that's not what Jason did. Feet spread, he stood tall in the stern, the outboard's control arm canted up into one hand so he could both steer and turn the grip to adjust the throttle.

He tickled the power to hold the boat steady against the current, not going anywhere. I could see him surveying the river, gauging the depth, plotting things out.

Then he edged that boat out into the river, moving it as slow and careful as an old lady on ice skates. As much as the river cascaded past the boat, Jason held it against the rushing water, bobbing here and there, but overall steady and smooth. He slipped past riffles and rocks, sometimes on the low side, sometimes above. At one point he went thirty or forty yards upstream, picking his way across. Then again he tried a passage downstream from us. The river powered along, but Jason matched its force, sometimes easing with it, sometimes dancing upstream.

He slipped and inched his way across, twirled out of a backwash or two, gyrated against narrow channels where the river went hard between boulders, and the boat skipped, bounced, and darted along.

Jason went across that river the way you'd tiptoe barefoot across a floor strewn with broken glass, one small, cautious step at a time.

It took him the better part of a thirty minutes to reach the other bank, and when he did it was as if all of us watching let out our breath at the same time.

Then Hicky spoke up: "He made it over, but with a man in the boat it's going to ride deeper, won't be that easy to frisk about like he done."

Nobody had anything to say to that.

I was watching through the glasses as Jason spent a bit of time with the guy, wrapping him in the blankets he'd brought over and so on. Then he got him situated in the boat and shoved off from the far bank.

About that time another vehicle came backing down over the river rock. This time it was the white SUV belonging to Elizabeth Manygoats. Liz had been a medic in the Navy and she was the closest we had to a doctor in this part of the country. It was Conrad Harper and Kenny who'd gone and got her, of course. None of the rest of us fools were anywhere near to thinking that Jason Goodwin might actually go across the river and come back with a man who needed medical attention.

We watched as Jason navigated the boat, now just a bit lower in the water. Yeah, he brought that boat across the river so easy wasn't no doubt he had it charted out.

It went smooth as anything, and then all at once, no more

than thirty feet away from us, Jason eased the boat around the downstream side of a sizable boulder and the boat's keel seemed to catch on something, maybe a submerged rock. At the same time a wayward current caught the hull and the result was the boat tilted hard over on the upstream side. As it did, Jason's passenger grabbed the dipping gunnel and hoisted himself to that side of the boat, maybe wanting to see how far they had left to go, or maybe scared of the sudden pitch. The standing wave behind the big rock got purchase on what little freeboard was left, and pulled the side of the boat down the last few inches and dumped the boat full of water in less time than it takes to say it.

The guy got soaked, and started howling something fierce, and Jason was shouting at him at the same time. I couldn't understand what either one of them said, though I figured the passenger was yowling get me the hell out of here and Jason was probably yelling shut up and sit down you damned fool.

For a few seconds the boat wallowed like a drunken whale not knowing which way was home. Then, three-quarters full of water but kept afloat by the built-in air compartments, the river caught it and the boat began to slide downstream with the current, the prospector hanging on to keep from being washed away and bawling his lungs out.

Hicky Johnson beside me muttered, "That'll be an end of it. They're finished."

When he said that I'll tell you true, I felt like turning to Hicky Johnson and grabbing him and throwing *him* in the river.

Instead, I just stood there and watched.

To this very day I have no idea what I would have done in that situation, and I dearly hope I never have occasion to find out. But I can tell you what Jason Goodwin did. Standing knee-deep in water in the back of that boat he gunned the throttle wide open, which shoved the back end of the boat down and brought the bow up so the water sluiced in a wave to the back of the boat where a bunch of it sloshed out over the transom. Jason pointed the boat towards us and it plowed ahead, scraping and bouncing over shallows, the outboard whining at top speed and kicking up when it hit the bottom.

When the boat got within grabbing distance, a bunch of the boys who had waded out grabbed it and hauled it up on the rocky beach. Then me and Dickie Bear and Morgan Chavis picked up the soaking wet prospector, who had quieted down now that he was on land, and run him up the rocks and into the back of Liz Manygoats SUV that was sitting there with the back end open and Liz on the blankets waiting for him. Morgan slammed the trunk lid down and Conrad Harper drove that prospector away from there.

That's what he turned out to be, a prospector. From what I heard, he was thirty miles upstream or so when he dropped a big old pine tree across a narrow part of the river. Since the opportunity was right there, he figured he'd go across on that tree, not that hard to do stepping among the branches, and take a look-see at what was on the other side. Prospectors are always wanting to see what's on the other side of whatever's in front of them. Of course the ice and water piled up against that tree, and soon pushed it back against the bank, and the prospector's bridge back across the river was gone. By the time he got to the spot across from us, he was scratched up and bruised, had hypothermia, and was about starved. He wouldn't of lasted through one more night.

Dickie, Morgan, and I came back down to where a bunch of the boys had gathered around Jason Goodwin. I could tell from the way he held himself that he didn't really need the boys to tell him what it was he'd done since he already pretty much knew it.

After a couple minutes the boys figured that out and headed back to the general store, but there was something about the way Jason Goodwin stood there that let me know he wasn't quite finished. He reached into his pocket and handed something to Kenny Harper, who was smiling up at him.

Jason said, "Go ahead."

Kenny reared back and threw it hard, and as it went out, arcing high over the river, you could see it turning in the air, a silver coin of some kind, maybe a fifty cent piece, maybe a silver dollar.

Hicky Johnson standing nearby said, "What was that?"

Dickie Bear answered him. "The river gives you something, you better say thank you."

"Well that's the dumbest thing I ever saw!" Hicky said.

Dickie Bear give him a long look and turned away, and as he went he tossed a final remark over his shoulder: "Maybe that's why you never catch so many fish."

Jason Goodwin went back to running the Standard Oil terminal when he wasn't prowling the countryside, and in case you're interested, Conrad Harper and his boy Kenny did indeed put up a broadcast radio station, and if you don't believe me you can tune it in for your ownself if you're ever out in this neck of the woods.

As for Hicky Johnson, I never seen him again. Somebody said he lit out the next day, headed up to Dutch Harbor to get work on a crab boat, and I guess that might be true. All I know for sure is he never came back anywhere around here.

About "Call"

This was one of the few times I took an event someone told me and turned it into the whole story. I published it in six installments on Amazon's Kindle Vella service. It's still up there. I like to think it makes a good bedtime story for kids.

I got the story over lunch.

Walter, Ken and I had lunch once a week for four or five years. Walter had gone to college, then law school, and practiced law for several years. He decided he didn't like it, got a master's degree in individual and family counseling, and did that until he retired. At one point Walter had joined the Army Reserve, and as a lieutenant, led a platoon of the supply company during the Los Angeles Rodney King riots of 1992. Walter had a pretty good crack at three occupations: Lawyer, soldier, mental health professional, but he said what he really wanted to be was a curator. He couldn't help it, he collected things. He had a collection of about 15,000 ballpoint pens, and a beautiful classic Mercedes Benz coupé he kept in pristine condition. Walter passed away in 2021. Now it's just the two of us at lunch.

Ken has a degree in electrical engineering and became a

partner and vice president of engineering at a high tech company before he retired. A couple things make Ken exceptional; one is that he built an airplane in his garage. He has a nice home in the suburbs with a wide two-car garage facing the sidewalk. Neighbors walking past would sometimes ask Ken what he was working on.

"I'm building an airplane."

The neighbors always said the same thing: "You can't build an airplane in your garage." For a while it was our catch phrase.

It took Ken three years to build it, and now he flies it several times a week.

The other unusual thing about Ken is that he couldn't read until he got into the eighth grade. Then something seemed to turn on in his brain. I have no idea whether it might be true or not, but I think Ken might be somewhere out on one far end of the autistic spectrum, and maybe the spectrum stretches so far that we're all on it. When you're having a conversation with Ken, it's not noticeable, but once in a while he'll turn away and he'll be gone for a second or two. Somehow, knowing Ken, having him for a friend, gave me permission to write Ruthie the way I did in story 11, *Negative Twenty Questions*, later on in the book. But maybe I'm on the spectrum too. When I was in the third grade they had my hearing tested because they thought I was deaf.

At one of our lunches, Ken told Walter and I the story of the guy marooned on the other side of the Copper River. Ken's father was an electrical engineer, had worked for NBC in Chicago, and was expert in commercial radio. He moved the family to the Alaska backcountry to build a radio station dedicated to religious programming. Ken was a kid when this story took place, so he didn't provide many details. For me the newcomers moving into the community to build a radio station became a secondary element of dramatic tension in the story, not just the people who do the courageous thing, but the outsiders who step up.

I spent a few weeks writing it. I had visited Alaska several times, so I wasn't intimidated by the setting. When I left for college, the last of four kids to leave home, my mother, an R.N. with a master's degree in public health, joined the U.S. Public Health Service and was assigned to the Tlingit village of Angoon, on Admiralty Island. I spent a week with her there on Christmas break from school. Later she was transferred to Palmer, Alaska, just outside Anchorage, and I made a couple trips there, too.

It was on one of those flights to Alaska that I looked out the window and saw the mountain ranges the way I describe them in the story.

The exact location of the story is nebulous because it's invented, as are the characters, though Ken did mention the manager of the Standard Oil terminal. Some of the details in the story are fictitious, including the throwing of a silver coin into the river as thanks. I tried to make it sound authentic, it might even be something a superstitious person might do, but take it from me, it's a toy airplane in a snowbank.

I printed out two copies of the story and saddle stitched them into booklets and gave them to Walter and Ken the next time we had lunch. It was only then that I realized what a huge mistake I had made. I fictionalized someone's story and then gave them a copy of it. What if they hated it? What if they were completely insulted and offended by what I had done? This piece of stupidity might have cost me the friendship of two people I valued. What an idiotic thing to do, for God's sake, don't ever do that again, I told myself. And I never will. I might steal your story and write it, but I certainly won't give you a pre-pub copy of it.

But in this case they liked the story, so that was a happy ending.

Show and Tell and the Hook

It's one of the drum beats for new writers: show don't tell.

And it's wrong.

Show don't tell is a misquote, and a misunderstanding. Supposedly, Chekhov said, "Don't tell me the moon is shining; show me the glint of light on broken glass."

With that, Show Don't Tell became a shibboleth among writing groups.

What no one seems to notice is that in his own stories, Chekhov used plenty of tell. For example, take the beginning of what might be his most well-known story, *The Lady With the Dog*. (You can read it for free on Project Gutenberg).

The first 500 words are all tell. It's only when we get to "One evening he was dining…" that we arrive at the first scene.

What Chekhov actually said in a letter to his brother was: "In descriptions of Nature one must seize on small details, grouping them so that when the reader closes his eyes he gets a picture. For instance, you'll have a moonlit night if you write that on the mill dam a piece of glass from a broken bottle glittered like a bright little star, and that the black shadow of a dog or a wolf rolled past like a ball."

Chekhov was talking about imagery—so that when the reader closes his eyes he gets a picture—and the mistake of summarizing and generalizing, as opposed to providing the reader with the details that bring a scene to life in the reader's mind. It's the details, the specifics, that grab the reader, that make a story both vivid and plausible.

In the hands of someone who knows what they're doing, or even someone who's not so good at it yet, "tell" can work well. Read the beginning of any number of Lee Child novels and you'll find a whole lot of professional tell.

The assumption is that "tell" isn't a good way to start a story in a way that will hook the reader. In the chapter on exposition in Alexander Mackendrick's book, *On Film-Making*, he points out that exposition certainly can be dramatic when it's in the context of a dramatic scene. For example here are the opening paragraphs of a story by my colleague, Frank Ladd, that was published by Akashic Books, used with his permission. The story is called *Falls Road*.

I lived on a farm on Falls Road in those days, a shortcut mile over hay grass and nettle fields to school. After class I'd hike across the playground to a pinch in the tree line. This was September of 1967, and I was fourteen. A girl didn't think twice back then.

Two sentences of exposition set the scene, then the end of the third sentence and the fourth sentence set the hook: she was fourteen, a girl didn't think twice back then. This is one of the ways, as Alexander Mackendrick points out in *On Film-Making* that exposition becomes dramatic. The hook could be made stronger if the line "A girl didn't think twice back then." was changed into the next one-line paragraph. But does it need to be made stronger? Wouldn't that be telegraphing too much? That's a judgement call for the writer.

With the hook set, the story continues with more exposition, delaying what the reader has sensed is going to happen, before a scene break and a change in focus to the other characters that are about to play a part in the story.

> *The trail cut through autumn growth, sloping down to a train bed that ran through town and along a gravel trench, before rising again to a thicket of scrub. I followed a fence behind the Shelburne Museum, past the blacksmith shed and the Ticonderoga, then north to the IGA parking lot. Beyond that, town land and empty meadow. Most days this saved me fifteen minutes home.*

~

> *The boys hid where the dirt path dropped to the railroad tracks, shielded by elm and drunken maple.*

Is the reader hooked, wanting to find out what happens next, even though it may make her uncomfortable?

If your story opening is exposition, figure out how to render it into dramatic exposition. There's always a way. And don't worry if you're telling the story. After all, stories have always been told.

7

That Which More Often Than Not is Left Unsaid

TRE—SHORT FOR TREVIGNE—TURNED out to be way more fun than I expected.

Monday morning rush hour, the first morning we rode together, hurtling down a Southern California freeway, locked in commute-struggle with a couple dozen thousand others, three lanes in our direction teeming with cars and trucks, a shiny undulating necklace draped across brown baked rolling hills, everyone doing eighty with three car lengths in between.

Which accounted for my tense forehead and sweaty palms. It's what you do twice a day in order to have the sort of life that interests and rewards you and is also good for raising kids. One gets used to it.

Tre nodded at a white Toyota 4Runner within scant feet of the car ahead, flashing its headlights. "Look at that asshole. What a tailgating creep, as if he expects the guy in front to move over, which he couldn't even if he wanted to."

As we neared the interchange, traffic slowed and tightened. When we pulled alongside, Tre checked him out: "Blue shirt, tie,

Hitler mustache. I'd say he's a fascist and a proctologist, an obsessive who wants to climb up everyone's ass."

I'd met Tre the Saturday before at a backyard get-together organized by the Homeowner's Association Welcoming Committee. I'd just said hello to her when a friend of mine, Wally, who managed an Ace Hardware store, asked her what she did.

Tre was tall, six-one or so. She gazed down at Wally's balding head for an uneasy amount of time, then said, "Research into causal opacity."

He frowned.

"The invisibility of causes."

She gave him a narrow-eyed stare, the way I'd seen guys in the lab examine a thin layer chromatogram when they're figuring out retention times.

She went on, "The incremental development of ideas and the concomitant creation of definitive theory."

"I think Sylvia is waving at me," Wally said.

"You scared him off," I said to Wally's retreating back. "What was that you said?"

"Just a bunch of shit I talk when I don't like someone."

"You don't like Wally? He's okay. His kids play with my kids. We watch Monday Night Football in his garage. He springs for pizza."

"Don't trust him, that's all."

A week later word went around that Wally was leaving his wife and two boys. Talk was he had a girlfriend on the side. I wondered if Tre had picked up on something about Wally none of the rest of us noticed, some nanoscale trace of expiring retention. Did Tre, or anyone for that matter, have that capacity for perception?

I never got around to asking her about it.

A couple months before, Tre and her husband, Wes, a highway patrolman, had rented a condo two blocks from Linda and me and the kids.

When I told her I worked in Technology Park, she said, "Hey, me too. We should ride together."

She gave me her card. Trevigne Tibett, PhD. "Call me Tre. Most people do."

She was tall, rangy, dark hair pulled back in a ponytail. She wore a pink cardigan sweater and white pleated skirt. They didn't match, but on the other hand they didn't exactly not match, either. She was in her late twenties or early thirties, younger than my thirty-five, and attractive in the way I've noticed smart women often are, her face open and alive.

I don't know why we have to categorize women the way we do. Or rather I do know, the genetic imperative is dominant, after all, but then there's all of today's cultural dissonance.

Anyway, with that patina of perception and awareness, she looked, to sum it up, *interesting*. So, of course she was someone I wanted to talk to.

As I chatted with Tre, my wife, hovering at the potato salad, gave me a wink. We do that. Ever since we met in grad school, Linda and I have been a pair bond, so that's it for us. Actually, there's a neurochemical basis for our sort of attachment, it's been described by Kaplan, Lancaster and Gangestad, if you're interested. Sooner or later someone will get around to interrogating samples at the molecular level and figure the whole thing out. In the meantime, Linda understands all too well my predilection for the dissimilar, the unlike, the disparate, which is both how I am, and what I've ended up doing for a living, so she's okay with it when I run across a woman I like talking to.

From the first Monday morning driving together, Tre called me Driver.

Her morning greeting: "Hey, Driver, how they hangin'?"

She'd grown up with three older brothers, and she had a mouth like a long-haul trucker—a long-haul trucker who was analyzing signal processing for speech recognition.

"Who the hell are you doing that for?"

"NDA."

It was her reply to all questions beyond the most superficial: Non-Disclosure Agreement.

"If I told you who we were doing it for, you'd start to wonder why they were looking into it, and that's exactly what they don't want—some autistic-spectrum geek like you wondering, because sooner or later you'd come up with what you thought their edge might be, and they don't want any bastards like you thinking about their edge."

We couldn't talk work, but we talked everything else. This was back when Obama was running for re-election against Mitt Romney.

"Here's the question," she said on one of the days we discussed politics, "Do we go for Plastic Man, or will we be staggering around in a daze four years from now wondering who is John Gault? Some fuckin' choice."

We had no idea, back then, the bizarre twist the future of politics had in store for us.

We'd been riding together for about six months when the morning came that she didn't have anything to say.

After five minutes I asked, "Are you going to just sit there? I might fall asleep at the wheel."

I felt her look over. "I think we should talk about having sex."

It had been there. In addition to being damn smart and a lot of fun, I couldn't help seeing her on a physical level. I mean, I'm a guy, with everything that implies.

"In general," I said, "or each other?"

"You and me," she said. "Us. I think we should talk about doing it."

My stomach flipped.

Linda and I had been together for eleven years, married for eight, and all that time I'd been out in the world, at the office every day, to the East Coast a few times a year, conferences and meetings, trips to Taipei, Hong Kong, Guangzhou. You ran across women you liked, women who kicked you hard in the amygdala, a few women who let you know it was a possibility despite the wedding rings. The same thing always stopped me. I pictured how I would feel when I got home and looked into my wife's eyes when she asked, "How was your trip?" I pictured the total trust on my son's face in a snapshot on my desk. He was four, carrying my birthday cake in from the kitchen, the candlelight illuminating his face like a cherub in one of those paintings in the Uffizi.

For me it was nothing principled, high-minded or honorable. I didn't have religion. It was simple: I knew I didn't want to feel the way I knew I would feel, and I knew I would feel that way for a long time, probably forever.

"I'm not really serious," she said.

"You're not?"

"Of course not. Jesus. My husband carries a gun for a living, we'd both be dead. But just between the two of us, what if we did do it. What would you like to do most?"

I finessed it. Even if we were only talking, it didn't feel okay. Finally I gave up a couple things. "Just hypotheticals," I said.

"Of course, just hypotheticals. Well, here's what I'd like, hypothetically."

She proceeded to tell me in the plainest possible terms, using the crudest most direct language, exactly how she wanted to be fucked—not made love to, "None of that romantic shit," she made clear, "I'm talking about good old-fashioned multi-positional pleasure fucking"—and what she'd like to do to me as I did those things to her—all hypothetically of course.

When we got to her building, she laughed as she got out. "That was really fun, Driver. Congrats, you stayed awake the whole time."

Awake? I was vibrating.

When I picked her up that night she started in again. "Hey, if we worked for the same company, know what we could do? Say we're in a meeting in some conference room, and our chairs are close together..." She started with wandering hands under the table and went on to elaborate trysts in the supply room—"There's a box of rubber bands on a shelf, those wide ones"—I never would have thought of using rubber bands that way. Then she went on to the kitchenette, bananas, packets of Sweet'N Low, crackers, peanut butter, candy bars melted in the microwave—it was a very well-stocked kitchen where she worked.

When I got home Linda was at the kitchen sink. I caught her from behind.

She used our old line: "Is that a banana in your pocket or are you in love?"

"It's not a banana," I said. "Where are the kids?"

I kept my arms around her as Linda called Mackenzie's mom, to make sure our kids stayed there another hour, "Feed them a snack or something," she said. I could hear Trisha laughing on the other end.

A half-hour later we rolled apart and Linda said, "It's times like this I wish I smoked."

It was something we read or saw in a movie back when we started together: the three best things in the world, a drink before and a cigarette afterwards.

"Okay," Linda said, sliding an arm across my chest, "it was great and all, but you need to tell me what's going on."

I told her about the conversation with Tre, all the details, the whole thing. When I finished she was quiet for a minute.

Then, "It was all talk? No touching?"

"Not so much as a fingernail," I assured her. "So, are you mad?"

"Not really," she admitted. "Not if it's just talk and doesn't go anywhere."

"It won't," I said. "It won't go anywhere."

A playful tone came into her voice. She took hold of me in a certain way.

"And I get the benefit of it?" she said.
"You get *all* the benefit of it."
"Starting tonight?"
"Especially starting tonight."

If you've never considered it in depth, here's something that may surprise you: sooner or later even sex talk can run thin. It's not like the infinite variations possible with something like, say, sonata form in the hands of someone like, say, Bach.

The second week of talking about screwing we began to invent scenarios for doing it as we drove in traffic at speed. She would straddle me, but the question was, facing me or facing forward, and who would handle the steering wheel? And where would legs go? Tre posited the reaction of other drivers.

"Toyota 4Runner Tailgate Asshole would hang on our butt," she said, "then come alongside to see if what he thought he saw was really going on. Then he would try and get behind us again because he wouldn't be able to help himself, but by this time somebody else would be back there, eyes bugging out, and they wouldn't let him in. They'd bump fenders, it would be like one of those crashes in *The Fast and the Furious*."

"How big do you think the accident would be?"

"Oh, shit, who knows? It would be colossal. The way these fuckers drive? Maybe a hundred-car pileup. Survivors would keep their lips buttoned, no one would admit anything. Nobody wants to be responsible for being a sleazy voyeur and making a bunch of people die."

Not long after that a Long Island hedge fund offered to triple her salary, and Tre and her husband moved east. I puzzled over that for quite a while: a hedge fund and voice recognition? And that much money?

We still exchange Christmas cards. This year, as usual, she added a note: "Hey Driver, keep it in the high dollar lane."

"Tre was a strange one," my wife says each year when the card arrives.

Strange and puzzling.

Tre was gone, but she left a legacy. From time to time when we're at a party or out with friends, and the conversation is less than scintillating, Linda will slip up beside me and whisper an explicit pornographic suggestion in my ear.

So now we've got a reputation: we're the couple that leaves early. Our friends are too nice to say it, but I can tell they think we've turned into a stodgy old couple that can't stay out past ten-thirty or eleven.

Which brings up another of the things I never got around to asking Tre: was that the outcome she intended when she started the sex conversation? Did her mind work like that?

A question I'd never gotten around to asking. But had I asked, I was pretty sure the only thing I would have gotten from Tre would have been one of her smiles that said, figure it out, Driver.

Commitment to the Scene in "Left Unsaid"

This story was published in *Magnolia Review Magazine*, Volume 4, Issue 2, July 2018. I was a little surprised when it was accepted for publication. Though there are fun elements in the story and some lively writing, fundamentally the story is inconsequential, mostly I think because I could never come up with a strong ending, so it sort of tails off, as some popular songs do when they haven't got a good ending either. If you haven't got a good ending, that usually means you don't have the right beginning. It seems to me now that the elements weren't there for a strong ending. There isn't any fundamental dissonance or incongruity that calls for resolution, at least not one I could come up with.

My cardiologist, Dr. Charlat, is responsible for this story. He persuaded me to enroll in the physical therapy program at Scripps Memorial Hospital in La Jolla. Five mornings a week, I drove the 15 miles or so of the freeway described in the first paragraph to the outstanding health facility at Scripps Memorial Hospital, La Jolla, where the suppliants were wired up to EKG monitors and followed a program, moving from machine to machine, like pilgrims doing Stations of the Cross. I did it for a year. It wasn't an onerous commute, but it was a commute, and it wasn't the most fascinating part of my day. It got me thinking—if I could have someone ride along with me, who would it be?

Once I started to think that it would be fun to have a woman ride-along, I thought it would be interesting to try to write the characters as real smart people, something I hadn't done before. Then I thought it would be fun to have a short story with a long title, like the famous Raymond Carver story, *What We Talk About When We Talk About Love*, which, as it happens has a character that's a cardiologist, but I didn't know that at the time.

But my version (naturally) would have to be the opposite of what we talk about when we talk about love, so I thought I'd make it about what it is we *don't* say when we talk about love, at least, when we talk about it in literary journals.

I hit on the beginning, the description of the commute, right away. As I've mentioned elsewhere, my usual mode is to go for the opposite, whatever that might be. For commutes the typical editorial attitude is an aversion to them, how wasteful they are, how demeaning and mind numbing for the driver, all valid points. So I took the opposite, pointing out the lifestyle that the commute makes possible. I wanted a good strong image at the beginning, so that's what I worked at creating, and I hit on a vivid metaphor capped with bitter reality to end that first paragraph: *a shiny undulating necklace draped across brown baked rolling hills, everyone doing eighty with three car lengths between.* I knew when I wrote it that editors would like it.

In early versions of the story, Tre was named Tree. I'd run across some woman on some writing board who used the name Tall Tree, and I liked the idea of someone who characterized themselves that way, so I remembered it and used it in early versions of the story, and then shortened it up.

I'd heard about chromatography, it's used in DNA fingerprinting, though I only had a vague notion of how it worked, so I looked it up on the internet and got to retention times, which was all I needed and "guys in the lab" is the nail that makes it real in the story. When I worked for a pharmaceutical company, sometimes on my way to interview one of the scientists for an article in the annual report, I would walk through a lab, the benches and glassware, the centrifuges, the hoods. I'd taken a semester of chemistry in college that included qualitative analysis in a lab, so I understood that workplace. Then the word retention, unusual to get used once in a story, gets mentioned again with *some nanoscale trace of expiring retention*.

How did I know to do that? I didn't know how to do it, but my character did.

Which calls for the transition to what I think of as *commitment to the scene*. This was something I discovered at one point when I was trying to figure out how to write fiction. First, here is what it isn't:

In reading other people's work, I would sometimes come across a passage in a story where the writer mentions something, say it's raining or a character sees a ghost. The story would go on from there with no further mention of the rain or the ghost or whatever it might be. It was as if the writer didn't notice what she'd written. A writer can only do that if they aren't really *inside* the story.

But I think the idea of commitment to the scene first came to me from something my father, the surgeon, said to me. For some reason, one day he decided I needed to know how to give someone a shot, stick a needle in their arm, maybe a vaccination or insulin, who knows what was going through the old man's head. Anyway, he said you give a shot the same way you put down a brick. That's all, he stopped there, no further helpful tips, as if to say you can figure everything out for yourself. My father went to medical school in the late 1920s to early 30s, probably a time when most of the medical school students had at one time or another picked up and put down a brick or two. But even if you have no experience with bricks, it's not hard to imagine putting down a brick. It's not something you can be tentative about.

In my mind, I changed the image of putting down a brick into the idea of driving nails with a hammer, specifically, driving nails so perfectly and powerfully, that it only takes a single blow of the hammer to drive the nail all the way into a board: bam! bam! bam! is how I wanted to write each word, like a hammer slamming a nail.

From these thoughts evolved my notion of commitment to the scene. When I'm writing, I'm three people: I'm the character I'm inside at the moment, and I'm also all the other characters and the setting, and I'm also the writer/director making the little movie run in the reader's mind. I have all those points of view available to me, and I'm perfectly comfortable, even enjoying the experience, because the images are feeding into my left brain language center from my right brain storehouse of memories and pictures. Yes, it's tiring, but we don't have nerves in our brains the way the nerves in our muscles communicate fatigue, so the tired-ness feels different, though it's just as real. There's more on this left-brain right-brain stuff in the essay *Imagination and Creativity* toward the back of the book.

How do you do this, or learn to do it? I only know one way. You tell your brain this is what I want you to do, this is how I want you to behave, and you put your fingers on the keyboard and start typing. The more you do it, the better you get at it, just like anything else. At first it feels hopelessly awkward and clumsy, and your brain will tell you that it can't do this, it doesn't want to, this is a pointless waste of time. It's just like the first time you tried to do anything from playing the piano to hitting a ball with a bat to learning to ride a bike to going off a diving board. It feels clumsy and awkward and dumb at first, but you have to understand those feelings are inevitable, and keep on going.

In the case of asking your right brain to chime in, you can't feel whether or not it's working, whether or not you're getting better at it. You can only tell that from the output, from what happened today compared to last month when you put your fingers on the keyboard.

8

Schoolboy

When we were fifteen, Gary Curtis and I started to make crank telephone calls, and we accidentally found a girl—her name was Darlene—who I thought might love me.

Ask a kid why he does any stupid, annoying or malicious thing. He'll tell you he doesn't know. But I know why we started in on the crank phone calls: Loneliness and girls. It was something to do, and it was fun.

In the afternoon we walked home from school together, stopping at my house, the first one on the way, because my mother, the public health nurse, didn't get home from work until six or six-thirty.

Gary was a carefree joker, a skinny easy-going kid with tousled brown hair and a wide smile, and I was pretty much the same except with shorter hair, glasses sliding down my nose, buck teeth, not so verbal, certainly not as socially adept.

It's not easy to talk about myself, even the self of so long ago. I was certainly lost. Stumbling along, day-to-day, basically cheerful with a hope that someday things would become as clear for me as they appeared to be for the adults around me: My mother who had gone back to school to get her master's in public health, my father the doctor and his new wife up on the South Hill in Spokane. Everyone had lives they more or less understood; they all gave every appearance that they knew what they were doing.

I had no clue.

My mother moved us there just in time for the beginning of the school year and Gary was the only friend I'd made. His house and mine were aligned next to each other on a flat, treeless street, prefabs thrown up across acreage that had been orchards. It was out at the end of the Spokane Valley; they had named the town Opportunity.

Well, you can't fault the developer; there was a lot of hope in the air. World War II was over, it had put an end to the Depression, and everyone knew something a whole lot better was on the way. Had to be better, couldn't be worse.

Gary and I were on our own for entertainment on those long, hot afternoons of early autumn. So we started to make crank calls. We took turns, a certain amount of one-up-man-ship involved.

This was long ago, in the days of dial telephones and telephone books. We would look up the number of a liquor store or cigar store, dial the number and when someone answered ask, "Do you have Prince Albert in the can?"

It was a brand of pipe tobacco that came in a metal canister.

When the proprietor said yes we would shout: "Let him out he's stinking up the joint!" and hang up.

Browsing through the phone book we discovered the name Takashita. Operating in our adolescent haze this became take-a-shit-a.

Every afternoon we dialed the Takashita number. The phone was answered by what sounded like an elderly Japanese lady with hardly any English. "Yes?" she would say, her voice querulous.

"Mrs. take-a-shit-a?"

"Yes?"

"Do you?"

"Yes?"

"You do? You take-a-shit-a?"

"Yes?"

"How often do you take-a-shit-a Mrs. take-a-shit-a?"

"Yes?"

After we made our usual calls asking after Prince Albert and harassing poor Mrs. Takashita, we dialed numbers at random, trying to engage whoever answered in some inane conversation. That's how we found Darlene.

She went to a high school on the other side of the valley, and she wanted to talk. Prince Albert and Mrs. Takashita went out the window. We took turns, handing the phone back and forth, pretending to be cool guys of oh, maybe eighteen or so. The past year in chorus I'd gone from an alto to the bass section. I put on my deepest, smoothest voice.

Stumbling across Darlene was kind of wonderful, because up to now neither of us had figured out how to do it, talk to girls. Sure, we'd talked to our sisters, to little girls when we were growing up. But now girls weren't little anymore. Some kind of tectonic shift had taken place; we were all wobbly. One thing was for damn sure: If I had been able to talk to girls, I wouldn't have been wasting the afternoons with Gary making crank phone calls. I would have been hanging on the fence at the tennis courts watching a beautiful dark-haired girl named Joanne scamper back and forth in little white shorts.

With Darlene it seemed as though we had accidentally blundered onto the one thing we longed for, the mystery that our budding male intuition told us was somehow the source of everything: the possibility of love.

Each day after Gary left I stayed on the line with her until my mother's car crunched up the gravel driveway. There seemed to be no end to what we found to say to each other, yet I can't recall a word. I'm sure it was the same thing teenagers are messaging and Instagramming today.

Someone once said, (wrote, actually), I think it was Somerset Maugham, that at fifteen a boy is still half a barbarian.

What, only half?

That certainly fit me. I was trying to discover the essence of things and people. Knowing so little, I could see only what I felt, and that the most elemental, the raw wants and needs. It felt exactly like what I didn't understand it was—a force of nature, something disturbing that was better kept tucked away out of sight. So I wasn't able to imagine the less than cataclysmic circumstances that might have brought Darlene to the state she was in.

Of course I had no sense of how easy it is to get one's life fucked up; the minor byplay of interpersonal stupidity, social recklessness, cultural folly, they were all beyond me, would remain so for a long time.

In my mind Darlene was a voice, an ethereal princess. I could sometimes, during a pause, hear her there, on the other end of the line, breathing. I treasured that faint sound, imagining us together somewhere, under a blue sky in a meadow, I with my eyes closed, her mouth close beside my ear, the whisper of her breath.

She felt it, too, I could tell. Can't you always tell? It was there, hovering. Sooner or later it had to happen: we decided to meet.

She set the place, the parking lot in front of a row of stores on Sullivan Road, halfway between our two schools.

Did I know where that was?

I could find it.

Good. She would be waiting tomorrow at three, a green two-door Chevrolet.

A car! Good Christ in heaven! So many things could happen in a car!

I called the bus company for routes and schedules.

The next day I told Gary I had to go to my father's house after school and caught the bus on Sprague Avenue. The wheezing diesel put me down across the street from the meeting place, fifteen minutes late.

The green Chevrolet was there, backed in facing out toward the road, just as she said it would be. Through the windshield glare I could make out a shape behind the wheel.

I had worn my best clothes, a long-sleeved shirt, my good corduroy trousers, both of them too heavy for the hot day. I could feel the perspiration trickling down my ribs.

An occasional car whizzed past as I considered catching the next bus home, but I realized I would have to cross the road to the bus stop to go back the way I had come. And since I had to cross the road anyway…

Come on, I said to myself, she likes you, she even said she likes you.

My eyes were fixed on the shape in the glare of light, the beautiful Darlene. I couldn't see anything else as I crossed the asphalt and then the gravel parking lot. It was certainly Darlene, a girl alone in a green two-door Chevy, blonde hair, it couldn't be anyone else.

I paused near the driver's side door and in an instant took in everything: The mascara streaks on her face where she'd been crying, the rat's nest of her hair, the baby wrapped in a blanket on the seat beside her. I caught the faint odor of diapers and milk. Darlene wasn't pretty at all. She gave a kind of muffled sob, a Kleenex pressed to her mouth, looking down the road the way the bus had come. Her hope was so transparent, so pathetic. He would come, the nifty guy with the deep voice, tooling along in a nice car, a confident guy—a man, really—who would wipe those tears from her cheeks, who would make everything better, solve all the problems, whisk her and her baby away to a better life.

And that certainly wasn't me. If there was ever one thing I knew in an instant, I knew that.

She didn't even turn her head to glance at the kid whose gravel footsteps paused by the side of her car.

I kept walking. Past the car and through the door into the variety store, where I stood behind a display of penny candy and looked out the plate glass window at the green Chevy.

I was in that store, I don't know, maybe a lifetime. Certainly forty-five minutes, maybe an hour. A stout woman in a flowered apron, her gray hair wrapped tight around her head, followed me around, probably wondering what kind of criminal enterprise the sweaty kid was cooking up as he wandered the aisles, always returning to look out the front window.

I saw what I saw, and seeing it, what I had felt for Darlene was turned back upon my own inner life. I saw the link between us, I saw things as they existed in themselves, as if walking through a museum for the first time, yet with no larger understanding of the idea of museums.

I saw the abiding unhappiness, the yearning, the promise.

Me and Darlene in the same boat. Hers maybe a little farther from shore than mine, but both of us drifting on the same waters. Wrong steps, inevitable disappointments.

Even as these thoughts went through my mind I couldn't bear to think them. I didn't want to know.

No matter how long I waited in that store, shadowed by the suspicious shopkeeper, it seemed that Darlene was determined to wait.

Finally I couldn't stand it anymore, I gave up. I bought six Tootsie Rolls, a Baby Ruth and an Almond Joy and walked out of the store carrying the candy in a paper bag, evidence that I was just another shopper, certainly not a person that someone might be waiting for.

I walked past Darlene, afraid to even glance her way, stood at the bus stop, my back to her, without turning to look even once.

I turned away from her the way one turns from a photograph of a third-world child with a bloated stomach, not wanting to see, not wanting, even, to remember what one has seen. There's nothing you can do about it so why torture yourself by thinking about it?

I was so young, so stupid, so helpless.

I felt so lost.

Such a schoolboy.

Using Biography to Write "Schoolboy"

Schoolboy was published in *Magnolia Review Magazine*, Volume 4, Issue 2, July 2018, the same issue that published *That Which More Often Than Not is Left Unsaid*. The editor, Suzanna Anderson, gave me a choice, publish them both in the next issue, or one at a time in succeeding issues. I figured what the heck, put them in together, so she did.

I wrote the story because I'd noticed that so many of the short stories in literary journals had a significant biographical component, people were writing about their lives, so that was what I set out to do. The first part is right out of my freshman year in high school.

My three older sisters had all left home to get married and I think my mother wanted to get out of her hometown, Madison, Wisconsin, which was filled with her sisters, her brother, her uncles, her aunt, their families. She'd gone to the University of Wisconsin in Milwaukee to get her master's degree in public health, and she got a job with the Kootenai County health department in Coeur d'Alene, Idaho. Coeur d'Alene is about an hour or so from Spokane, Washington, where my father lived with his replacement wife, so my mother found a rental house out at the end of Spokane Valley closest to Coeur d'Alene. The school, Central Valley High, was terrible, and according to Google Maps, it's no longer there. The first day of school involved hazing the incoming freshmen, whacking the new boys with paddles. The highest status boys were those on the boxing team, bullies with tattoos (yes, they had a boxing team, and that's right, the inmates were running the asylum).

My mother might have had some idea that moving us closer to Spokane might encourage some relationship with my father, but that didn't happen. I don't remember seeing him at all during that school year, and only a couple times during my next three years of high school, when my mother moved us to Coeur d'Alene.

So Gary and I, a couple bored kids, put the available technology to work with crank phone calls. All that stuff, even the stupid Prince Albert joke, the reprehensible racist calls to the Takashita number, my crush on the dark-haired girl, were just as they happened, and even coming across Darlene, that was all true. I don't remember if Darlene was her name. The conversations with her never progressed beyond maybe half-a-dozen phone calls.

By the time I got the story to that point, I dreamed up the rest of what I needed in order to turn it from a vignette into a story, though I did remember at that time I had a heavy long-sleeve shirt and corduroy pants that I wore at Thanksgiving and Christmas, so that was a detail drawn from memory.

By the time I got halfway through the final scene, I knew where I wanted to end, a simple last line, *such a schoolboy*, carrying more weight than one might expect of a pedestrian phrase. I could hear in my mind the intonation of that phrase, the way I wanted it to sound in the reader's mind. It was a matter of figuring out how to make that happen.

I think at the time I was reading *The End of the Affair* by

Graham Greene, so that might have influenced the mood I wanted to precipitate.

Conflict Big and Small

I walked out of the office one evening, and the thought occurred to me: What anyone can know is limited by one's ability to speak about it (think about it). I was working for a small agency, and had a business card that said I was the creative director. I spent my days writing copy, sometimes writing it, other times cranking it out. What I really wanted to do was write fiction. God knows why.

I knew then and know now the same vocabulary everyone knows surrounding stories. This is mainly the vocabulary we learn in English classes, supplemented by what we've picked up from blogs, books, writing sites, and at grandpa's knee if one happens to have that sort of grandpa.

So far as fiction went, I understood then what everyone probably thinks at one time or another: A writer should put conflict (whatever that means) into their work.

I went along, never thinking about conflict, not examining it, until I ran across a paperback called *On Film-Making* by Alexander Mackendrick, forward by Martin Scorsese, and the first chapter, *What is a Story?*

I bought the book because I found myself suddenly writing, producing and directing industrial videos for clients. Up until this time, everything I'd worked on as a copywriter was for print production, which because of my experience with magazines, I understood fairly well.

Then the small and specialized agency I worked for was acquired by one of the major accounting and consulting companies in the country, at the time called KPMG Peat Marwick. The Marwickians, I came to call them. It was like a Dickens novel. After work we toasted one another in pricy bistros, calling out, "Tax *avoidance* is not tax *evasion*."

Not really, I made that up. But we did have a pretty good time.

A client wanted a video that explained their 401(k) plan to employees. I was the creative director, so it was all mine. I wrote the script for a 20-minute video. Once the client okayed the script, I hired a production company with a sound stage, cameras, and crew to produce it, and with the help of the production company, hired the actors. The production shot on a sound stage in one day, and the principal thing I learned from the experience was that from then on I would direct and edit the shows myself, which I did for another half-dozen or so productions. One year, one of the videos I wrote, produced and directed won the regional Emmy for the Pacific Southwest Division. You won't find a record of it, this was 1991, pre-internet.

What I didn't expect when I started reading *On Film-Making* was a tutorial on conflict not just in movies, film and television, but on the essence of story. *What is a Story?* is one of the first chapters in the book, essential reading for someone who wants to write fiction, as is the next chapter on exposition and as is the whole rest of the book. When you are writing a story, like it or not, you are the producer/director. The more you know about those roles, the better writer you'll be.

The phrase that best summed up what I learned from this

book was written by theatre critic William Archer (1856-1924): *Drama is anticipation mingled with uncertainty.*

Anticipation mingled with uncertainty—what we're talking about isn't conflict, it is *dramatic tension.*

So the goal is not to "get conflict in there somewhere" but rather make readers feel the way you want them to feel—anticipation mingled with uncertainty.

Open almost any Amazon bestselling novel, for example, say *The Last Man* by Vince Flynn and read the first sentence. You'll find anticipation mingled with uncertainty. This novel is typical genre, entertainment for those who like it this way. But Mr. Flynn has technique. Consider this sentence: *Something he did not want to consider.* The character is conflicted and the reader, like it or not, is going to feel anticipation mingled with uncertainty.

How much has the technique, anticipation mingled with uncertainty, changed over the years? If you read the opening paragraphs of Raymond Chandler's *Blackmailers Don't Shoot,* copyright 1933, *Black Mask Magazine,* you'll find the anticipation of a jaw of stone, a sensitive mouth, clothes as though they had a soul of their own, not just a doubtful past. You'll find letters costing ten grand, and the twist, the advice to Miss Farr—that's not too much.

The uncertainty is in the disparate elements, how they will weave together to provide us a satisfying result. We're confident we're going to get a satisfying result because of the terrific originality of that first paragraph, the author letting it all hang out, not holding back, saying yeah, it's a formula yarn with a formula detective, but it's going to have stuff in it like an almost diffident hand and if you don't like it, to hell with you, the author isn't explaining anything. The writing has an absolute feeling of commitment and confidence. It speaks directly to something we are subliminally looking for, letting us know we're in the hands of a voice we can trust.

Raymond Chandler understood perfectly what he was doing,

creating anticipation mingled with uncertainty. There's a quote I think is by him (my colleague Ross Murdock probably knows it) saying that a reader will read a good detective story even if the last chapter is missing. The point being that everything along the way keeps the reader feeling anticipation mingled with uncertainty, and that's what the reader wants to feel, that's what the reader is reading for.

A Report from the Baby Lab

Our local art house/foreign film theatre used to run a trailer that had a line narrated voice-over in several languages, concluding with a woman, who in a British accent said, "The language of fil-um is universal."

(A fil-um is something quite distinct from, and far superior to, a mere movie.)

I always made fun of the line, saying it to my wife in my awful Indian accent, my terrible Irish accent, my appalling English accent, and sometimes, if I timed it right, catching her a little by surprise, getting a derisive laugh, or at least a smile.

And then, this afternoon, I realized, all kidding aside, it's actually true. Yes, the language of film *is* universal. But it's not the language of film that's universal, it's the language of *story*.

My experimental work in the Baby Lab has shown that this universal language only requires a few gestures and a surprisingly simple soundtrack, which is optional.

You can see for yourself how it works if you happen to have the right experimental conditions available. My test subject is a chubby female aged eleven months named Avery. The investigational procedure takes place during her noon meal, when she is sitting in her high chair with the tray before her waiting impatiently for lunch.

The test begins when the producer-director-writer taps the fingernails of two fingers on the tray in front of her, gaining her attention. Then the two fingers begin marching this way and that, just a few small steps, accompanied by a little toot toot toot marching music. The musical quality of the tune doesn't seem to matter. But we here at the Baby Lab like our experiments to have production values, so the narrator softly breathes a little cheerful melody that provides a mood and rhythm for the marching fingers.

Avery's attention immediately fastens on those two fingers. Throughout the rest of the experiment, her focus stays fixed; never once does she look up at the narrator, breaking the fourth wall between the play and the audience. This gives additional meaning and depth to Henry James's "willing suspension of disbelief."

Clearly the suspension of disbelief is not merely willing. It is abject surrender. Even that, we believe, after numerous experiments, doesn't go far enough. It seems to be lapsed into, willingly or not: it is attention surrendered in a relaxed state.

The fingers march for a moment then approach one of Avery's hands resting on her tray. With a little hop they are on her hand and marching up her arm. She doesn't move as this happens, yet her excitement clearly grows, the dramatic tension heightens, she almost seems to vibrate. This is it! And suddenly the fingers burrow beneath her arm and she wiggles and laughs. The fingers withdraw and Avery looks up at the writer-producer-director and bestows her version of a bouquet of roses: her look clearly says, do it again?

And so it goes, the same basic play with a variation here or there, again and again.

And now comes the boring part, and if you've read this far you might as well continue, there's not much more.

I think the little playlet works because it recreates in a safe way the fundamental fear that even an eleven-month-old child has of the near approach of an unusual creature of some kind. The immediate situation has an element of trepidation, yet clearly it is safe, for certainly Avery can see that the fingers are attached to Grandpa.

The basis for "story" is no more complicated than this. At the same time it is just this profound.

It's fundamental. It's pre-language, it's in-born. It's anticipation mingled with uncertainty. The Baby Lab has shown it to be so.

9

Making a Living

MEET NEW PEOPLE, JORDAN'S astrological forecast said.

He took the stool next to Jordan's at the bar of the Blue Parrot, said his name was Leon. He wore a blue baseball cap with yellow lightning bolts on either side. The cap was on backwards.

Jordan hated rubes who wore their backward hats everywhere. He hoped—in vain he knew—that this guy, Leon, might be something other than a Los Angeles Chargers fan. Maybe he was the forerunner of a cult just now emerging, a bunch of people who got together on weekends to illegally administer electric shock therapy to one another, maybe that's what the lightning bolts were all about.

Jordan loved the Blue Parrot. Loved it for its existential coolness outlined in hazy green and blue neon. If Albert Camus had summered in La Jolla, he would have been here every night. He would sit at a table in the back, order a Pernod, light a Gauloises, tilt his chair against the wall, a sardonic look on his face, and let the smoke curl from his mouth up into the nostrils of his thin, aristocratic nose.

Leon was nothing like Albert Camus. He was one of those straight-ahead twenty and thirty-somethings who seemed to be all of a piece, no doubts, no inner contradictions, no angst. The path of least resistance opened out before them like a great welcoming lowest-common-denominator freeway. He'd dropped out of high school to go to work as an apprentice meat cutter—a good union, good money. But it had its drawbacks.

"You have to put up with the smell."

Then he fell in with a guy who taught him how to smuggle cocaine. Now he had a box under his bed holding four hundred and some thousand dollars. He was pretty sure it was about that. Cash, maybe half hundreds and the rest mostly tens and twenties because you just didn't see that many fifties these days.

"Of course I only tell you this because you have no idea where my bed is. But now," Leon pursed his lips, "I've gotta get serious. I need a smart guy who can help me get my money laundered."

Jordan's nervous system went on full alert at the mention of the money. "You know," he said after an interval, somewhat hesitantly, because he didn't want to overplay it, "I just might be able to help you out." Great holy hell, his mind had spritzed on the possibilities.

"Yeah? No kidding?"

"Yeah. I know a guy," Jordan said, thinking ten percent was forty thousand dollars.

Maybe Leon was on the naïve side, but he was shrewd, too. Jordan took in the chubby cheeks, the cherubic look of a guy who had been in high school not that long ago. But more than that, he saw, tucked back in the shadow of Leon's brow ridge, the flat, assessing eyes of an experienced felon. This wasn't the first time Leon had braced a guy in a bar.

If there was any chance at all of making some money off this dude, Jordan knew he had to make this good.

"This guy I know, he's a lawyer," Jordan said, off-hand. "Real smart son-of-a-bitch."

Keep it casual, try to let this guy know the money is really sort of minor league. Four hundred grand? BFD.

"Let me ask you," Jordan said, "I meet a lot of you guys. I mean, this is San Diego, thirty miles from the border, and I'm a writer. You're about the twenty-seventh *trafficante* I've met, and every one of you guys has the money in a box under the bed. Is it the drug that makes you all think alike?"

"No, man, no, you got me wrong," Leon jumped on the defensive. "I move the stuff, I don't use the stuff. It's business, that's all. A little weed, that's no big thing, but that's it."

"I didn't mean to imply you were just another runny-nosed crackhead, or anything. I believe you. You're that rare breed, a businessman. A serious and dedicated young capitalist. It's just that I hear so many of these cocaine and weed smuggling yarns, all these stories about car chases through the back alleys of Tijuana and Mexicali. I saw a promo for *Ordinary People* on the Turner Network the other night? I thought it was going to be about dopers on the run."

"Yeah?"

It went right past him. He had one thing in mind.

"This guy you know, this lawyer, think he'd be interested in helping me out?"

"Well, I dunno. You want to meet him?"

"Sure," Leon said. "Might as well." But it was way too late to pretend indifference.

"I could give him a jingle."

They traded numbers.

They had another round then Leon had to leave, had to see a guy. Jordan knew he'd got what he was looking for, a smart money man to launder his cash. He'd come looking among the people he thought had money, knew about money, the people in La Jolla.

"Rich or poor, skinny or fat, ugly or beautiful, we're all playing the same game. We're turning away from the old traditional values, family values, following in dad's footsteps. The drug experience is a really big part of it. It's here, we're going to have to learn to live with it."

Tommy Murdaugh leaned his thick forearms on the wooden table. He had been second string at USC twenty years before, a linebacker. The arms were still impressive.

The three of them were at a back table in Melvin Deli, the downtown sandwich shop on West F Street where attorneys and paralegals grabbed lunch.

Jordan had called Tommy Murdaugh the next day, told him the deal: a kid named Leon, a dealer with a cash problem. "And listen, I need something out of it. A finder's fee. Ten percent."

Tommy laughed. "Oh, hell why not? Bring him by the office, we'll do lunch."

Jordan buzzed Leon's cell, told him eleven forty-five and gave him the address.

The waiting room was right out of a bishop's library in Renaissance Italy, thirty foot ceiling, tall narrow windows so law clerks could shoot arrows at attacking messengers with subpoenas, the whole place lined with carved walnut and reeking of pedigree and a pallet-load of dollar-denominated negotiable securities somewhere in a sub-basement. Jordan watched as Leon picked up a back issue of the Kiplinger Newsletter with a photo of a billionaire's yacht on the cover.

As for himself, he whiled away the time admiring the silky thighs and deep cleavage of the receptionist, a lanky dark-haired beauty who sat behind an oak refectory table the size of a wing off a Piper Cub. From time-to-time she refreshed the display by re-crossing her legs, her micro skirt riding up, heavy breasts brushing the polished table as she bent to her work.

Jesus, he thought.

Tommy emerged from an inner sanctum, paisley tie askew, the sleeves of his button-down shirt rolled up, a cheerful grin on his flushed face. Tommy looked as happy and prosperous as if he had just convinced a querulous widow that half the estate was a reasonable probate fee. There was a faint odor of whiskey on his breath that the mint didn't quite mask.

Jordan had known Tommy for years. After USC, he went to Stanford Law, then married the daughter of one of the partners. Tommy and his wife moved in the right circles, he had every opportunity to follow his father-in-law to the top, but he was lazy, had a taste for booze, fooled around not quite discreetly. The only thing his son-in-law status bought him was tenure. At forty-six he was still only an associate, reporting to a partner five years younger.

At the deli, they ordered sandwiches and Cokes and took them to a table in the back. Jordan watched Tommy wolf down an egg salad.

Leon, clearly nervous, leaned across the table. "Is this conversation privileged? Are you my lawyer?"

"Gimme a dollar."

Leon took out a roll, peeled off a hundred dollar bill and handed it to Tommy. "You're my lawyer now."

"That's right, kid," Tommy laughed. He tucked the bill into his shirt pocket.

Leon told him about his money, and then Tommy took the floor.

It was all such bullshit, Jordan thought. Tommy sounded exactly like what he was, a semi-functioning alcoholic.

Leon was boring, too. He didn't pick up that nobody was impressed with his C-note client status. A dumb kid from a dumb place called Lemon Grove. The convo at the bar, the fake camaraderie, it was all in the cool jazz and the way that damn neon at the Blue Parrot gave everything a quarter of a turn to the left.

Tommy got down to it. "I would have to talk with the part-ners before I could represent you." His voice had the full-bodied smoothness of a premium scotch. "Now don't take this wrong, but I'm almost certain they wouldn't allow me to handle your case. Of course, even if I don't represent you beyond today, this whole luncheon is privileged."

Luncheon. What a crock. Jordan watched Leon's face fall, read him like the big E on the eye chart. If Tommy Murdaugh was on his side, his problems were solved. But Tommy wasn't gonna be on his side.

Jordan was disappointed, too. No transaction, no finder's fee.

"It's not a reflection on you or your particular lifestyle," Tommy said. "The partners are very conservative. I'm sure you understand. Don't take it personally."

Don't take it personally? How the hell else should he take it? How the hell should I take it?

But he smiled and nodded, and that was how it was left. Out on the sidewalk they shook hands and that was it.

In the days that followed Jordan did his best to find work. At a party one night, standing in somebody's kitchen, someone mentioned something about Tommy Murdaugh, how he had left his wife and kids. Jordan paid no attention, he had his own problems.

Then one day the phone rang and he had a corporate gig, a client in San Francisco. He had no idea how they'd gotten his name, and he wasn't about to jinx things by asking.

They flew him up for a meeting and handed him off from one guy to another in offices and laboratories, spent the day explaining exactly what they were after.

They were paying two grand, half up front plus expenses and

Jordan and a photographer named Don Shapero were on their way to Phoenix to do a brochure on a new contact lens.

They spent the day at the Biltmore Hotel, a stone hulk in the middle of a golf course, some kind of landmark designed by Frank Lloyd Wright. Jordan talked with the ophthalmologists who had developed the lens, the polymer chemists in charge of manufacturing and the dispensing opticians who were the money behind the deal. Shapero said he missed his wife, flew home that afternoon.

Since he was on the client's dime, Jordan stayed over.

The next morning he was sitting in the coffee shop of the Camelback Inn, trying to ignore the canned music and pondering a weird facet of human behavior. All of the contact lens experts, to a man, wore glasses. Whenever Shapero lifted his Hasselblad to snap a shot for the brochure, the contact lens guys all whipped off their specs. Evidently if you were developing a new contact lens, you had to pretend you didn't wear glasses.

But it wasn't as weird as when he looked up from his English muffin and saw Tommy Murdaugh sitting across the restaurant. The woman close beside him on the banquette was the receptionist from the law office.

Tommy looked right at him, smiled and waved hello.

Remembering the gossip, Jordan felt his mind unroll on one plain simple fact: Tommy had stolen Leon's drug money.

Tommy spoke to the brunette, then came over to his table, pulled out a chair.

"Hey! What are you doing here?"

Jordan went right to it. "So you got away with Leon's box of cash."

Jordan watched him cave.

"I couldn't help it." Tommy grinned like a naughty boy. "He made it too easy for me. He called me the next day, practically begged me to take the money. What could I do?" Tommy shrugged. "I said I'd talk with him—really, that's all I was thinking. He brought the money in two suitcases. I mean, listen, right there in a Safeway parking lot with people walking past, with his own hands he took the suitcases out of the trunk of his Mustang and put it them the backseat of my Benz!"

The confession came easy. Jordan could see how forgiveness had always been bestowed on the jock, the son-in-law. He was wearing a Rolex Jordan hadn't seen before; his face was puffy and raw, the look of a newlywed, happily pussy-whipped.

"How much was there?"

Tommy hesitated an instant too long. "Two-fifty and change. But what the hell, it was like a gift. Listen, I figure I owe you something. Five grand, okay?"

Five grand. Jordan felt like he was embroiled in a scene from an old Richard Widmark movie.

"You're a shitty liar. You think Leon didn't tell me how much money he had? I want fifty thousand dollars. Right here, right now. And consider yourself fortunate that I'm not a greedy person."

Tommy wheedled and squirmed. Finally Jordan took out his cell and scrolled, as if he were looking up Leon's number. It was a pretty good acting job, worth fifty grand. For all he knew the number Leon had given him was a cheap throw-away. Druggy boy probably had a box of throw-aways he kept right next to his box of money.

The brunette, Judi (with an "i", she said), came over to sit with him while Tommy went for the money.

They looked at each other in silence for about twenty seconds. Jordan could tell from the way she had walked across the coffee shop that she knew exactly how hot she was. She was wearing tennis shorts and a skimpy sleeveless blouse that somehow she had not managed to button much above the waist. She wasn't wearing a bra and her breasts were delectable where they disappeared, her nipples outlined against the white fabric. Jordan felt his forehead twitching.

He had to say something.

"What kind of contact lenses do you wear?"

She told him about her contacts, giving her long, dark hair a flip.

"Tommy is a lucky guy to have found someone with your spiritual quality," he said to her. "You must have a great deal of inner strength."

Where was all this coming from?

She gave him a warm smile and he felt her foot brush against his leg under the table. His imagination tumbled... if things were different...

"What are your plans, you and Tommy?"

She told him they'd found a motivated seller with a Seven-Eleven store in Scottsdale and this morning a realtor was picking them up to go look at condos. The Seven-Eleven had gas pumps, and the condo had its own satellite dish with two hundred and sixty four channels.

They must have had the money in their room, all counted and tied in bundles, because Tommy was back in no more than ten minutes, the cash wrapped in a white plastic laundry bag.

Jordan kept an eye on the mirror as he drove the rental back to the airport in case Tommy, the aging action figure, decided to follow along and see if he could get the money back.

He found some rock 'n' roll on the radio and turned it up loud and kept time on the steering wheel.

"It's a beautiful morning in Phoenix," he sang, making up his own melody, "if you don't mind the smog."

He watched the rearview and sang and considered Tommy Murdaugh and his lady.

What an unimaginative, second string chiseler he had turned out to be. The real measure of a man was what he did once he made his big score. Onward to a future of achievement and satisfaction, a Seven-Eleven store and a condo in Scottsdale. What a sucker. Inside two weeks Judi would be screwing the pro at the tennis club while poor old Tommy was down at the Seven-Eleven, counting quarters from the slushy machine.

It would make a hell of a movie for TV. Jordan could see one of those sensitive, boy-next-door actors playing Tommy, and this season's hot new teeny singing sensation in her first big dramatic vehicle as Judi. A revealing human drama, sure to grab a big share of the up-scale demographic if they pushed it with the right hype.

Jordan tried out a few tag lines before he hit on one he liked, giving it the cadence and dignity of a network promo:

"He was a lawyer turned thief, she was a receptionist with great legs. They had it all—convenience store shopping and satellite TV. And suddenly they faced the ultimate challenge—all those expenses and short fifty grand." He cackled with laughter.

Jordan sat at the counter of the Colony Kitchen restaurant in San Ysidro, the last freeway exit before Mexico.

He checked his watch and looked around, scanning the few customers. The meeting was set for midnight, he was fifteen minutes late and his guy wasn't here.

He ordered breakfast.

The source was a disgruntled employee of the Immigration and Naturalization Service, the Border Patrol, who had agreed to take him into the evidence rooms in the tan building that straddled thirty lanes of almost-always backed-up traffic waiting to cross the entry point into the U.S. from Mexico.

Urban folktales had been floating around for years about shelves jammed with illicit contraband, torn plastic garbage bags leaking amphetamine and methaqualone capsules that crunched underfoot, marijuana strewn all over the floor from the holes the field mice gnawed in order to escape from the burlap bags where they were trapped at harvest time.

The guy said there was two hundred thousand pounds of marijuana in storage and the place was an unholy mess.

It wasn't a great story but it was a story he thought he could sell.

He looked around, making sure he hadn't missed the guy in his Border Patrol outfit, his *migra* suit.

Either he would show up or he wouldn't, either he would call again or he wouldn't. Jordan didn't really care because everything in his world was once again spinning the right way round.

The contact lens job was done, they'd paid him, reimbursed the expenses, and he had the fifty grand from Tommy Murdaugh. That bundle of money was stashed, still in the Camelback Inn laundry bag, under the backseat of his car, the safest place he knew. No one would bother that old tin can, an aging Pontiac with a bad case of parking lot rash.

When his food came, Jordan ate slowly, savoring the scrambled eggs, the bacon, the toast, plenty of refills on the coffee, marveling at how good it made everything taste when you were rich. This must be how the fat cats felt, always lighthearted, no cares, no worries. No wonder they always looked so plump and merry.

Jordan looked around, making sure his guy hadn't come out of the men's room.

Oh, well, what the hell, there was always tomorrow.

He waved the waitress over for a refill and from the inside pocket of his jacket took out a pamphlet. *Secure Investing for the Long-Term: The Smart Way to Save.*

Jordan smiled, thinking how, on top of everything else, he had been reimbursed for his expenses at the Camelback Inn. That was deeply ironic, he would love to get that into a story.

His nose buried in the brochure, Jordan had no idea Leon had just swung open the restaurant door. Even if he'd looked up at that moment, he might not have recognized the drug smuggler he'd met at the Blue Parrot, since Leon now wore the full dress uniform of a Marine corporal, hat squared away, the visor pulled low over his eyes. A chubby high school girl with blonde ringlets in a pink formal with a white gardenia on her wrist held Leon's arm. It was true artistry the way he moved his cocaine across the border.

The instant he recognized Jordan at the counter, Leon turned and pulled the girl back outside.

"What? What's going on?" Crissy was miffed, he'd promised her a burger and a shake.

"Shut up."

He was paying her a hundred bucks to spend three hours, driving down to Tijuana then back again, nothing else, not even a handshake at the end of the evening, just the ride. She would do what she was told.

Moving fast, he walked her back to the Mustang, put her in the passenger seat.

"Keep your mouth shut," he said. "There's an extra fifty in it for you."

He went to the back of the car, opened the trunk and rummaged until he found the tire iron.

The parking lot was out behind the restaurant. Leon picked a dark place at the back corner of the building, up against some Oleanders that were blooming, fragrant in the night air.

He had to wait nearly thirty minutes. He was ready to wait all night—hell, he was ready to wait forever—standing there, hefting the tire iron, thinking how much he wanted to hurt that smart-ass son-of-a-bitch.

Standing in the dark, he thought about hitting him in the face, in the head, again and again, just battering the bastard right to death, right there. He pictured his brains spilling out of his crushed skull.

No, he needed to ask a few questions.

When Jordan came strolling past the corner, Leon stepped out and hit him in the chest with the jack handle, taking a full two-handed swing, giving it everything he had, hoping just as the steel bar connected that it would pop the bastard's heart like a water balloon.

Jordan stood there and swayed, and Leon loved the shock, the breathless wide-eyed look on his face.

"Little surprised to see me, huh?" he said, and stepped in and kicked him in the balls as hard as he could.

Jesus, that was just about the most satisfying feeling in the world. Leon smiled, having a really good time.

Jordan lay curled on the asphalt driveway, retching, bringing up everything he'd eaten.

Leon looked around, making sure they were alone. He stepped into it and kicked Jordan in the midsection. Jordan was vomiting and whenever he caught his breath, kind of half-sobbing, curled up, holding his balls. Leon didn't have a clear shot, the kick wasn't as satisfying as that first one. Still, it felt pretty damn good.

A guy came out of the restaurant walking toward them. Leon held the tire iron down along his pants leg against the dark blue of his dress uniform on the side away from the guy.

"He okay?" the guy said as he reached them.

He was older, looked like a working stiff on the swing shift.

"Yeah," Leon said, "my buddy had a little too much tequila. I'm gonna let him get it out before I take him home."

The working stiff wasn't coming anywhere close to the smelly mess around Jordan. He nodded and went on his way. Leon stood over Jordan and watched as the guy got into a car and drove off.

When the coast was clear, Leon bent down and took a grip on Jordan's hair and yanked him to his knees. It was like pulling on a rag doll. He tapped him lightly alongside the head with the tire iron.

"Where is my money? Where is that shyster lawyer?"

Jordan made a blubbering noise.

Leon tapped him a little more firmly, a little love tap.

"Either you tell me and tell me right now where my money is, or I'm gonna fucking kill you, asshole." He meant exactly what he said. Leon was surprised at the venom in his voice; he had thought he was cool, he didn't realize he was like that, in a total killing rage. He looked around, making sure they were still alone. He should do him, he thought, just on general principles.

"My car," Jordan blubbered, "in my car."

"And the lawyer, where's the lawyer?" The steel bar made little taps against Jordan's head, almost by itself, keeping time with the blood Leon felt pulsing behind his eyes.

"Phoenix," Jordan said, "Scottsdale," then he muttered something that Leon didn't catch.

"What? Say that again!"

"A Seven-Eleven store," Jordan said. Leon could see he was trying hard to speak up.

"The fucker's got a Seven-Eleven store in Scottsdale, Arizona?" What a strange thing that seemed to be.

Through his hand buried in hair, he felt Jordan try to nod his head.

"Take out your car keys."

Jordan took them out and dropped them on the asphalt.

"Which car is yours?"

"Pontiac," Jordan answered, "green Pontiac."

That was all he needed, at least for now. Leon hefted the tire iron back and gave the asshole a nice crack on the head. It put him right out.

He dragged him over to the Oleanders and dumped him under the bushes.

The money, wrapped in plastic, was in the first place Leon looked, tucked under the backseat. Using the tire iron, he ripped the shit out of the inside of the car anyway, just for the hell of it.

He stood in the dark in his Marine dress blue uniform, breathing hard, the tire iron in one hand, the plastic bag of money in the other, looking over the tops of the cars in the parking lot at the Oleanders on the back wall of the restaurant.

He could go over there and kill him, just finish him off. It wouldn't be hard to do. It was about what he had coming. He glanced over at his Mustang, Crissy's blonde curls visible in reflected light. She could place him at the scene. He'd have to kill her too. It wasn't worth it. Let the bastard live, at least for now. Maybe he'd cross paths with him again someday. Time enough then to hurt him, hurt him real bad.

The next thing Jordan knew someone was helping him up. He couldn't see out of his left eye and his knees were weak.

"You shouldn't drink so much, man. All the beauty that ever existed in the universe is right here, right now—" the guy was saying, then, "Jesus, you're all bloody!"

Jordan peered at him. He couldn't tell if the long-haired kid was stoned or born-again, or maybe both, and he didn't care. Jordan pointing the way, the kid helped him over to his car.

The inside was destroyed. The headliner hung down in ragged tatters, all the seats had been sliced open and ripped apart. The rear seat had been pulled out, and of course the money was gone.

Jordan got in and slumped behind the wheel. The Samaritan urged him to stay cool and have a nice day and hurried across the lot to a van and drove away.

The stinging and whirling began to fade and were replaced with throbbing pain. The car keys were gone. Maybe Leon had thrown them into the bushes. He'd take a look in the morning if he was able. Or maybe he would call an Uber and go home and never bother with the car again.

He eased down, seeking a position that didn't hurt so much.

It was just as well that Leon had found the money. If he hadn't, he would have asked more questions.

Jordan could hear the traffic on the freeway. The pungent scent of sagebrush drifted in the window. He couldn't move. He'd stay here till morning. He would try to sleep, one side of his face drying to a crust, his ribs cracked and aching, a deep throbbing in his groin.

The itinerant wordsmith, having lost his money, having betrayed his partner in crime, spends the night with his aches and tribulations in a tired and raggedy old Pontiac.

Things were not working out the way he had hoped.

He'd tried, God knows he'd tried. The freelance gigs, the bohemian life, that had lost its charm.

So he'd ventured on a life of crime. Look where that got him.

That was it, he'd had enough. He was turning over a new leaf.

In the morning, somehow, he'd get home. He'd take some Vicodin left over from a trip to the dentist. Then, in a week or two or three, when he felt up to it, he'd call those contact lens guys in San Francisco, the pharmaceutical guys with the deep pockets. They liked the brochure, he'd see if he could get on the payroll.

He'd give commerce a try, he'd sell out. He'd try and sell out. Everyone always made it sound as if it were easy to sell out, as if all you had to do was give up and there it was.

Now he wasn't so sure.

Writing "Making a Living"

This was the first piece of fiction I wrote that had any success. It won the Ursus Press Short Story Contest ($750), then the weekly *San Diego Reader* bought it for $75.

I wanted to get a bit more mileage out of it, so with a few revisions it was published by the literary quarterly *West Coast Review*, a publication of Simon Fraser University, British Columbia.

The story began with an anecdote from a friend and lawyer, Tom Adler. He told me about a drug dealer that had walked into the office of the small law firm where he practiced seeking advice on how to launder the large amount of cash. Of course, the law firm turned the drug guy down.

I saw possibilities in the episode, but didn't know how to write it. So I took as a template, *Two Gallants*, a story by James Joyce that's in *Dubliners*. My story ended up having no relationship whatsoever to *Two Gallants*, except the two stories are episodic. I guess I just needed the reassurance of thinking it was possible

I think the story was successful, and holds up today to the

extent it does, because I had so much fun writing it—one cocka-mamie idea after another.

The first version was written in first person, and then I revised it into third person, I don't remember why. But I do remember vividly what I learned from that exercise: They aren't really that different, first and third. This was something I'd never read or heard of, so I think this experiment encouraged my independent exploration of the mechanics and techniques of fiction, which was the lasting benefit of writing the story, much more important than the money, though of course it didn't seem so at the time.

I wanted to write a rattling good story, that's what I set out to do, nothing more complicated than that. The meeting with the contact lens guys at the Biltmore Hotel in Phoenix was actually something I did. At the time I was working for Syntex Corporation in Palo Alto, and the company had purchased a contact lens company. Management wanted an article ghosted for the editor of *Contact Lens Forum*, where it ran in the April 1979 issue. Don Shapero and I flew over from Palo Alto, and in the photos that appeared in the magazine, none of the contact lens executives are wearing glasses. We stayed at the Biltmore. The Colony Kitchen restaurant was there in San Ysidro, just on the U.S. side of the border with Mexico, though I think it's gone now. I customized the parking lot situation to fit the story. I invented the stuff about the drugs stored in the building at the border, as well as a lot of other things in the story, including the characters, the law office and the receptionist.

I've made one significant change in the story from the one that was originally published, and that is to omit the scene break that occurs when Jordan is in the Colony Kitchen restaurant and Leon, the drug smuggler starts to come in the door. I took out the scene break, which is the traditional way to handle this change in point of view, and instead fashioned a transition from Jordan's point of view to Leon's. Did you notice this change in point of view when you were reading, and if so, did it bother you?

One thing I didn't invent, and that was the Blue Parrot, which also is gone now. It was down a flight of wooden stairs from Prospect Avenue in La Jolla. My wife and I went there once when Mose Allison was playing. It was just as cool as it is in the story.

Write What You Know

There's a vast difference between, three-dimensional, complicated, real people in real life, and a character in a story.

Stories mostly don't (and don't need to) reflect the totality of a character to the extent that a reader has a chance at parsing out the authentic from the inauthentic. For example, doesn't Ray Donovan ever stop to take a shower and change out of that black suit? Doesn't he get hungry, or need to pause sometimes on his way to club a miscreant and need to take a crap? No, he's definitely not real.

Stories are often about *how it feels* to be such and such a character in such and such a situation. And the feelings are universal and convey in a convincing way the authenticity, whether or not the writer has really ever been a desolate young woman, an arrogant teenage girl or a Mexican kid tossed into a jail cell.

I've never been or experienced any of those, but I've written and published them, and editors have taken the bait because I was able to get across how it felt to be them, at least convincingly enough, under those circumstances, with those editors, at the time…

As Lisa Cron writes in *Story Genius*, quoting Harvard psychology professor Daniel Gilbert,

"Indeed, feelings don't just matter, they are what mattering means."

At one level, fiction is similar to a magic trick, but a magic trick that draws on the writer's experience.

Who hasn't experienced rejection? Felt isolated and alone? Felt the disapprobation of a group of others? Felt a desperate and chronic loneliness? Been flat broke with no prospects in view? Questioned who you are and whether or not life was worth living? *Who hasn't felt like an outsider for one reason or another?*

If you're a writer, or someone who wants to write, chances are you have been there, done that. This is how I interpret the advice, write what you know.

A Preface to the Preface

The piece that follows is the preface I wrote to a book of mostly biographical stories written by George Hubbard Miller (1934-1982) and published as *Across This Silent Canvas*. You can find it online.

I edited the stories, some more than others (*Blackberry* was a hassle), generally got things into shape, and at the back added Hub's poems and a few pieces of our correspondence. This was back in the days when people wrote letters. (No, no, really, that's what people did, I know it's hard to believe.)

When he sent me the stories, Hub knew he was dying. When the package came, he didn't have to say anything, I knew it too.

The preface mentions that Hub was stationed at Fairchild Air Force Base, just outside Spokane, Washington, and I was still in college at the University of Washington in Seattle. From time to time I would call him up by dialing the number of the base, and telling the operator in my deep, authoritative voice, "This is General Spencer. I need to talk to Airman George Hubbard Miller." My calls always went through, the military is wonderful that way.

When I encountered all the machinations involved in publishing Hub's book, I sent copies and registered it with the Library of Congress, thinking that at the very least, the book will always be there. I thought no more about it. Then one day, a few months later, I got a phone call from a woman who introduced herself and said she was with the Library of Congress. I started to tell her about Hub, the composer, the ranch—she stopped me. "I know who *he* is," she said, "I read the book. Who are *you*?"

Preface to Across This Silent Canvas

I wish this could be only about Hub, but I can only make it about me at those times that Hub was there.

I can't vouch for the perfect accuracy of all the details, and (assuming you're not reading this as part of your dissertation prep) that's not what you really want to know, anyway. So I will set this down partly the way it was for me at the time, and partly the way I know now that it probably was, and you can have it for what it's worth.

I tumbled off the back of the turnip truck at the University of Washington the autumn of 1954, driving from Coeur d'Alene, Idaho to Seattle with a high school classmate who had a car.

I had thought that Reed College in Portland, even in those long-ago days a hotbed of the liberal arts, was where I should go, but Reed required an essay as part of its application. The summer I was eighteen beside Lake Coeur d'Alene life was just too sweet and easy to bother with an essay. So I was off to the UW, where a high school transcript C+ average, a check for tuition and a pulse rate were all one needed.

I had made what today I remember fondly as my first adult

decision when I chose *not* to go to the University of Idaho with the high-jinks-loving high school gang—I had a deep premonition that would be fatal. I felt the need to strike out in another direction. I didn't know much, but I knew there was an awful lot I didn't know.

Back in those days I was a jazz drummer. My idol was the impeccable Max Roach. Two of us, my pal the trumpet player and valedictorian Craig Kosonen and I, had outfits for serious evening wear modeled on the most stylish Mr. B—Billy Eckstine, the legendary jazz vocalist.

I signed up for the university marching band. The first day of band practice, I was surprised to find I was the only student who wasn't majoring in music. When this came to light, the band director gave me a sour look and a brief audition and then grudgingly let me stay. So there I was, the would-be jazz drummer from, of all places, Idaho, shown even during his first days at college to be a notable misfit.

I met Hub toward the end of that first week.

Reading Hub's piece *Blackberry* today, I can understand what he saw in me, since just two years before he had been the misplaced cowpoke from Eastern Oregon.

Hanging out with Hub was a world of unexpected experiences.

We would be walking down the hallway of the music building in the evening, and Jo, an intense piano major, would pull Hub into one of the practice rooms to help her with something she was working on. Gordy would ask Hub to come over and listen to a Chopin etude and help him with phrasing. One Saturday Hub told me we were going to Marlene's. I had heard the name, Marlene was a piano major who could *really* play, but that's all I knew.

We drove across Seattle to a house on Mercer Island with floor to ceiling windows overlooking Lake Washington. I waited on a sofa that felt like silk while Marlene played on a Steinway with the top up and Hub paced, smoking and listening. What the hell is this all about, I wondered, who is this guy?

Everyone wanted a piece of Hub's musical ear, his insight, his understanding. They listened to him as though he were one of the professors.

Hub dragged me along on many of these occasions, maybe for company, maybe for my further edification, or perhaps to keep the situation from veering too much from the musical to the personal. Because it was more than the music. I can still see him in his characteristic pose, elbow cupped in one hand, holding a cigarette beside his face, a light shadowing of beard along his jawline, that little half-smile he had and the look in his eyes straight at you while he listened, taking in everything. Then he would reply and as often as not he addressed on the one hand what you had said, and at the same time the subtext of your entire personality and your fundamental assumptions about life. Too often it seemed as though Hub understood more about you than you knew about yourself.

With music, with literature, with social institutions, with people, with everything, Hub played a game new to me: how perceptive can you be, how intuitive can you be?

For all that, when it came to jazz Hub was as square as they come. Here was a guy who called himself a composition major and he had never even heard of Thelonious Sphere Monk, much less the dress code of a hip dude at the clubs along Manhattan's 52nd Street. I called him Hube the Cube, or (once I had found out about Braque and Picasso) Hubist the Cubist, which was, I thought, the most appropriate moniker.

One weekend Hub took me home with him to Portland, where his family had moved from the ranch so his mother could receive the medical care she needed. For me Hub's family was like something out of a novel. His father, Earle, I was to learn during this and subsequent visits, liked nothing better than to sit down with the college boys and talk ideas. I always thought he would have been happiest as a professor of philosophy. Hub's mother, Marion, was quite ill with cancer. I was ushered into the room where she was propped up in bed, obviously weak, for a brief introduction.

Hub's brother, Jolly, short for Jolyon, was named after one of the characters in John Galsworthy's series of novels, *The Forsyth Saga*. Jolly was a handsome, charming star athlete at his high school. Hub's youngest brother, Lee, was the joker-clown of the family. But it was the open and loving warmth and pleasure that each family member so obviously felt for the others that was new to my experience.

And then, the next school year, Hub was gone.

"Where's Hub been? I haven't seen him lately."

"Didn't you know? He joined the Air Force."

"He what?"

"Quit school and joined the Air Force."

Those were the days of Universal Military Training, the Draft, for which we would all eventually become eligible. But Hub's move was unexpected and unexplained. One day he was just gone.

Hub was gone, but my education continued. Eventually, one early spring afternoon on the grass in front of Vernon Parrington Hall, I discovered the drama majors, a world in which I found an appealing combination of artistic activity, old fashioned pragmatism and certainly the prettiest girls on campus. I also started hanging out with O.D. Hale (1936-1993), a skinny kid from Eastern Washington, a poet, Phi Beta Kappa, who had an amazing way with girls. His poem about Seattle, a parody of Edna St. Vincent Millay:

> The mountains ring the city
> In variegated green.
> We know the names of towns beyond,
> The mountains lie between.

If mountains didn't rise there,
The names would seem less grand.
O isn't it a wonder
How the universe was planned.

I came home to my father's house in Spokane at the end of my sophomore year to find that Hub had moved into the top bunk in my room and had created for himself the role of fair-haired boy in what passed at the time for my family. The dogs, Wimpy and Susie, loved him, and my step-mother Maxine and my father, a physician and surgeon, liked him a lot more than they had ever liked me.

Hub had insinuated himself completely into my family with no introduction on my part, all on his own. In addition to the surprise of finding him there, becoming the favorite son had the added bonus of being a little joke on me, as if to say, Jeez, Bill, your family is so easy to charm and manipulate, why haven't you bothered to do it?

Hub was an enlisted man in the Air Force, stationed at Fairchild Air Force Base just outside Spokane. My father called him Airman Miller.

The Air Force trained Hub as an electronic counter-measures technician. As the ECM tech, Hub flew from time to time on missions in the B-36, mainstay of the Strategic Air Command. At that time the U.S. was flying secret missions probing the radar capability and weaknesses of Cold War threat Russia. The ECM operator was responsible for the early detection of the Russian radar signals so that the plane could fly out at the edge of their range, where the plane could read their radar signals, but they couldn't detect the plane. In the event a missile was fired at the plane, the ECM operator had various counter responses available. Hub told me about flip-flops and gates, the technology of the earliest computers.

It was an immersion in electronics in the Air Force, and

science around the house. The coffee table always held the latest issue of *Scientific American*, that month's editions of the *Journal of the American Medical Association* and the *New England Journal of Medicine*, as well as the odd copy of *American Rifleman* and *Field and Stream*. The glass-fronted bookcase in my room, which was really more the extra room where things were stored, held back issues of the annals of the American Radio Relay League, Boccaccio's *Decameron* that contained some pretty hot stuff and Kraft-Ebbing's *Psychopathia Sexualis*, a study of sexual perversity, remembered, when it's remembered at all, for his coinage of the term sadism. We might not have been much for displays of affection around my father's place, but by God we were pretty damn well-read.

One summer Hub and I drove from Spokane to the Double Key Ranch, five thousand acres in Eastern Oregon. We travelled along part of the route Hub describes in *Journey Home*. Hub said he needed to visit his horse, Tabasco.

Those were the days before CDs, before eight-track tapes, even before FM. For music we had only the little AM band radio and the skunky sound of a distorting speaker in the dashboard of an aging Chevrolet. But it didn't much matter, because the only stations available were broadcasting either the top forty pop tunes or (more commonly) country-western music.

For me the long, tedious parts of the trip, as the endless hills of sagebrush rolled past, were made even more annoying because Hub had no sympathy for my malaise. He told me how on some car trips when he was alone he would imagine Mozart, Beethoven or some other figure from the past in the passenger seat and his task was to explain to them everything that had happened since they died, starting with their questions about the car itself, the speed, the highway, the billboards and of course the country-western music coming from the radio. I remember he said that Beethoven was a particularly bothersome guest—because he was deaf, Hub had to shout whatever he said to him.

Hub had an unusual capacity to entertain himself. Sitting on the beach at Lake Pend Oreille in Northern Idaho where my father kept his boat, I would be in the doldrums, waiting impatiently for whatever was going to happen next, which I knew well enough was not very much, while Hub busied himself with the smooth glacier-and-river-rounded rocks. After a while I would look over and see that Hub had figured out how to stack this improbable material into a beautiful little model building that had kind of a Frank Lloyd Wright look to it. It's not just that he was able to enjoy himself and make something, but that he made something beautiful.

Hub told me—maybe it was during the trip to the Double Key—that he was never bored, that everything was interesting, and that he really didn't understand how anyone could be bored. He said that one time he had decided to try and experience complete and total boredom, so he planned an entire day, from morning to evening, doing absolutely nothing other than sitting in front of a television set watching daytime TV. It was the '50s. He figured, and I fully concurred as he told me this story, that this would be the most incredibly boring thing a person could possibly do. He said he started to watch the daytime soap operas and there wasn't much interesting in the content, but he began to pay attention to how one scene was designed to foreshadow and flow into the next, what the decision process must have been underlying a show or a dramatic construction. You can watch a soap opera, Hub maintained, and like a sort of cultural Rosetta Stone, extrapolate what the producers and writers assumed about their audience, and so gain an insight into their cultural assumptions, and therefore everyone else's cultural assumptions.

So as it turned out he wasn't bored at all by daytime television, but rather he found it somewhat intriguing.

Hub told me this story and I nodded and filed it away, wondering to myself at the time whether he had actually done that experiment, or whether he had just made it up in order to provide me with a little lesson in how to entertain myself. If he made it up as a clever instruction for Bill, then Hub's mind worked one way, but if he had actually undertaken that experiment, then his mind worked in another, perhaps more profound and disciplined way. Who in the world actually had enough patience and abstract intellectual curiosity to sit down and watch television all day (assuming, of course, they weren't some nitwit who actually liked daytime television)?

One of those summers after I had taken a creative writing class (the professor's wife had once dated Lennie Tristano, a blind pianist who played with Dizzy Gillespie and Charlie Parker during the bebop era), I was working on a one-act play I called *No Deposit, No Return*. The title was taken from the notification that at the time appeared on soft drink and beer containers, as the bottling industry began its long and losing battle against the impetus for recycling. I'd been reading Jean-Paul Sartre, Albert Camus and Andre Gide, and I thought it was a pretty cool title. I was sitting around the living room in the evening scribbling on a yellow lined tablet.

Within a day or so Hub brought out his own yellow lined tablet and announced that he, too, was writing a play. His was called *Into the Weathers of Space Go I Unrehearsed*.

I was chagrined; his title was so much more emotionally evocative and pregnant with possibilities than was mine. Mine was the dead-end, his was everything in the future. Hub further needled me by never allowing me to read any of what he was writing, while he got to read and criticize all my stuff.

When I started putting this volume together [The book of Hub's writing, *Across This Silent Canvas*], I at first thought that I would call it *Into the Weathers of Space Go I Unrehearsed*. But then I realized that however much I liked it, however affectionately I remembered it, it didn't fit. For one thing, by the time he got around to writing the pieces in his book, Hub knew well what the weathers of space portended, and he had had plenty of rehearsal. The tolling beauty of that phrase was really a recapitulation of his place in the world at that particular time: leaving the University, joining the Air Force, uncertain what would come next and unsure where he would land, like the wind-borne seeds of the thistle he describes in *Blackberry*.

In the spring of 1958 I graduated from the University. Not much was made of the event. My mother flew down from Alaska, where she was a nurse with the U.S. Public Health Service, and Hub drove over from Spokane. We went to dinner at a Chinese restaurant. That fall I was drafted into the Army. When I was discharged in 1960, I requested release at Fort Dix, New Jersey and caught the bus to New York, where Hub had moved with Jolly's help about six months before.

Hub and Jolly had been living in Seattle, where they had the old Chevrolet, the same one Hub and I had driven from Spokane to the ranch four or five years before. They had sold it for (I think the figure was) five hundred dollars to a couple of acquaintances who did not have the money at the time, but promised to pay in the future. A year or so went by with no payments made for the car. In the meantime, Hub decided to move to New York. So they called up the guys with the car, said they were moving, and could they borrow it. Since the guys had yet to make any payment for the car, they could hardly refuse. Hub and Jolly picked up the car, loaded their stuff into it and drove it to New York. It was still there, sitting on West 87th Street, when I arrived.

Those months in New York were a post-graduate education in mid-20th century culture. Hub's aunt, Gladys Miller, Earle's sister, had moved to New York after college, and she was now one of the senior people at Holt, Rinehart and Winston, a publishing company on Madison Avenue. She was editor of two magazines for the company, had been the interior designer who redecorated Blair House, the government guest house across the street from the White House, and she was the author of a well-received book, *Decoratively Speaking*. She lived in a beautiful apartment at One University Place on the edge of Greenwich Village.

Gladys received complimentary tickets to performances at Carnegie Hall and the Metropolitan Opera, and she gave all her tickets to Hub. We went to every event at Carnegie Hall, where Leonard Bernstein conducted the New York Philharmonic.

These were also the golden years of live drama on television and New York was its center. Every week we went to Gladys' apartment to watch *The Play of the Week* and *Playhouse 90* on her television set, and it was there we saw Samuel Beckett's *Waiting for Godot* with Burgess Meredith and Zero Mostel. Ingmar Bergman's movies were reaching the U.S., and *The Seventh Seal* and *Wild Strawberries* were playing on a double bill at a theatre in Greenwich Village.

We saw everything, and everything was there in New York to be seen, even Leni Riefenstahl's classic propaganda ode to Hitler and the Nazi Party, *Triumph of the Will*, the whole uncut thing. Some afternoons I would wander across Central Park to the Metropolitan Museum of Art, walk upstairs to the gallery on the south side of the building, sit down and look at El Greco's *View of Toledo*, just that one painting, nothing else. After a while I would walk home. The music, the movies, the television programs, the bars, the restaurants, the museums, the people—it was all grist for the mill.

Hub rented a second-floor-front apartment at 24 West 87th Street, just a half block from Central Park, and had enchanted Lena Staub, the little rotund landlady with a Middle European accent. "Helloo Meester Mee-lar," she would chime when she passed Hub on the stairs, and always want to stop and chat.

In *Little Brother* Hub writes, "Even at five years of age I could identify the emotional tenor of the performer from the sound of the instrument." I don't think that's an exaggeration. I know he could hear things before others heard them. He had a parlor trick I would cajole him into performing. As we walked down a New

York street, Hub could hold up his arms, like Leonard Bernstein in front of the New York Philharmonic, and conduct the sounds of New York—the car and taxi horns, the sirens, the crash of the garbage trucks, all the sounds of that notoriously noisy city. He would give the little upward ready move, then the cue and the taxi bleat would be there, echoing through the Manhattan canyons. For me and for others, we could at best wave a hand only just fractionally after the sound arrived. But somehow Hub could hear what was coming before it quite got there, or perhaps he was listening to the silences between sounds or picking up the city's tempo. I didn't know how he did it, I could never figure it out.

The following year, the Army reserves on my heels, I left New York. Jolly and I drove the old Chevrolet back across the country pretty much non-stop. That trip was a novelette in itself.

I wish I had kept a journal of those years and written everything down in careful Boswellian fashion. But to do that I would have had to have been someone else, and then perhaps those things we thought and said and did and played at might have been entirely different. Maybe not even worth writing down at all. So there you have it, just like Hub's opening paragraph in *Measles*, a paragraph that rings so truly with his voice, "The insidiously irritating irony of it all is that... no matter how much one knows, one never knows for sure."

Intro to The Bastard Died
On Me

The next piece isn't really much of a story, more of a vignette about what happened, what it was like, when I was working on Hub's book. When it was accepted by *Soft Cartel,* the editor called it an interesting experimental piece.

There's no need for an annotation, the piece itself describes how it came about.

10

The Bastard Died On Me

(In a major key)

SAY YOU'RE A WRITER, some kind of writer, and you come up with the perfect title for this thing you've been working on, and the next thing you know, someone steals it.

Well, of course they don't steal it because no one but you knows what it is, and you can't steal titles and ideas anyway because you can't copyright them. If you could copyright ideas Homer's descendants would be suing Clint Eastwood over *Iwo Jima*.

(Have you ever considered what a peculiar combination of sounds that is: Iwo Jima? You hear it, you see it, but not until you type it do you realize that it's just damn weird. You know it's some kind of a small jima—anything iwo has to be tiny tiny—but what's a jima? Do you think, possibly, it might be a penis?)

That's the kind of thing that bastard thought was funny, stuff that was totally off the wall.

Anyway, I had hit on the title. It was just what I wanted. It spoke directly to my market, the twenty and thirty-somethings sitting around Starbucks with earbuds dangling down unplugged.

The earbuds are out because this target demo of mine is listening to that particular music they play in Starbucks that, for me, characterizes their subculture. It usually features a female vocalist, mellow and creamy, no crescendo, no diminuendo, the melody a relaxed, featureless glissando. It's kind of mesmerizing, it's pleasant and it's often beguiling. It's what your psych prof might call *affective flattening*.

(Modulate to the minor)

I was putting together a book, not mine, pieces written by that bastard who'd died on me. I'd flown up to Seattle to talk to his brothers, and when the gathering broke up coming on midnight I realized I hadn't bothered with reservations. Rather than ask for a ride somewhere, I'd walked down the street to one of those aging fringe-of-the-inner-city cracked linoleum motels. The sheets were clean, not pristine and starched, like the ones at the Hilton in Hong Kong or the Plaza in New York, but clean. Despite appearances, I'm basically a blue collar type and clean is all I ask.

It wasn't the sort of place where you sleep in, phone down to room service and spend a lazy morning sitting near a sunny window with an English muffin, a pot of coffee and the *New York Times*. I was back on the street at six and the only place open was the Starbucks on the next block. (There's a Starbucks on every next block in Seattle, I think it's an ordinance or something).

I sat there with coffee and a bagel, making line edits to a manuscript that had been written by a musician and composer I had admired, a person who had been the brother I never had, who knew when he wrote it that he was dying. But you can't hold all that in your mind and get much done. I sat in Starbucks and listened to the music, looking up from time to time, watching them come in for coffee, wondering.

Absence of affect. Was it a choice favoring simplicity versus the ornate, plainness rather than embellishment? Was it because they toked a bit the night before and now they wanted everything velvety and uninvolving? Or maybe if everything is everything and it's all neither this nor that, you won't be disappointed, because after all, what's this is pretty much the same as what's that over there, and, ho-hum... whatever.

(Transition back to the dominant)

It took a while before I hit on that title for the thing of mine I'd been writing, just right for a first-person narrative for those kids at Starbucks—simple, flat, blunted affect.

Then a few weeks later, waiting for the start of Woody Allen's latest, the previews of coming attractions came up and there was my title, hijacked by Hollywood.

(Finish on a flatted fifth)

He died on me and left me here and I'm still pissed off about it. Now who's around to make fun of me when I start feeling sorry for myself about something stupid, like that dumb title?

When Your Story Needs a Language

There comes a time, and often it's quite early for writers of fantasy, where they not only want to build a world, but they want to create a language to go with it.

Not long ago, someone asked about this in a post, and my colleague Cliff Robison amazed me with his reply, which he gave me permission to quote:

> "If you're going to make a serious investment in linguistic world-building," Cliff wrote, "I recommend starting with a Zipf list of words, say 1,000 or so. Find the corresponding words in your invented language, and you should be able to navigate nearly anything."

What is a Zipf list?

Quick trip to the internet: It's named after the American linguist George Kingsley Zipf (1902–1950), who popularized it and sought to explain it, though he did not claim to have originated it. A Zipf list is a list of the most commonly used words in a language, ranked from most used to less used. It turns out there is a frequency common to languages: the most often used word will occur about twice as often as the second most frequently used word, three times as often as the third most used word, and so on. For example, in English "the" is the mostly frequently occurring word, and it appears about twice as often as "of", in second place, and three times as often as "and" in third place.

Cliff went on with his explanation:

"Next, find a few forms and rules. Do plurals typically end with -s/-es, or perhaps -i? with -en? Or do you follow the Indonesian trick of simply repeating the noun (Orang = person/man/woman, orang orang = people/men/women)? Do you repeat adjectives to emphasize "very"? Can groups of people be described by adding a suffix to an adjective, i.e., Russian -nik, semetic -im, mordor -ul?

"Now pick the order of subject-verb-object. Languages can be SVO (typical English), SOV (common in German or French), or even OSV (typical Japanese).

"A vocabulary of 1,000 words will enable one to read a surprising number of normal documents, notices, hand-bills, and the like; 3,000 words, and you're reading nearly everything that a secondary student would be expected to read, 5,000 and you're nearly fluent. Many writers, editors and publishers are said to have vocabularies of no more than 10,000 to 12,000 words.

"Thus, get the top 1,000 concepts that your aliens are likely to say, assign them some orderly sort of language-rules, make a crib-sheet, and you're off to the races."

I had to ask Cliff how he came up with all this stuff.

"I stumbled onto the Zipf list kind of by accident. I'm a really curious guy, and might be researching any old thing I come across at any given time. Also, I've always had an interest in languages. If I had to say where it started, it was probably with Rex Stout stories that mentioned Serbo-Croat, a language like nothing I'd ever heard.

"So I decided to apply the Zipf lists to language studies, and I came up with a slightly whimsical project that I called "1,000 Words." It's the top 1,000 words in Spanish, French, Serbo-Croat, German, and Finnish. To be honest, I speak Spanish slightly, French badly, and German almost not at all. But with a Zipf list and what seemed like centuries of editing and looking up words, I hammered out a lexicon for those five languages. Then I lost all interest in the project, partly because I was burned out from Slavic cases. If there are truly ten million names for God, every one of them is in Serbian, Croatian, or another Slavic language. Tata, Tate, Tati, and Tato all mean "Father," but Tatu means "Thief."

For more help on coming up with a language for your world, you might visit author Michael Tedin's blog that explains how to make an invented language sound natural: https://michaeltedin.com/worldbuilding-102-how-to-make-a-constructed-language-sound-natural/.

Intro to Negative Twenty Questions

In some ways, this is a pretty good story, but it's flawed, and I haven't been able to find a publisher for it. One editor said he liked the set-up, liked the characters, but it needed an ending.

I thought this was valid. I'd written a bunch of ending material, but had set it all aside. I'll include some of this stuff in the annotation after the story.

A reader for another publication sent me a nice rejection, saying so much of the story takes place in dialogue, he had the feeling he wasn't immersed in a story, rather, that he was watching other people being told a story. That's valid too for this reader, though it was his personal reaction and some readers might have felt otherwise. The story is written from an omniscient point of view, so it's natural that the reader feels like she is looking "at" the characters and events, rather than being immersed inside one of the characters, which would be typical of the third person point of view. But he did like Ruthie (but then, *everyone* likes Ruthie).

A note on writing an autistic character: I have no idea whether or not there is or could be a character with Ruthie's traits, but what seemed to give me permission was my friend Ken who is at the far end of one of the branches of the spectrum. He couldn't read until he got into the eighth grade, but then went on to get a four-year bachelor's degree in a scientific field and have a successful career. He's a smart, engaging person, and you have to spend quite a bit of time with him before you pick up on the very faint hints of who he might have been as a child. Somehow, for some reason, knowing Ken gave me the confidence to go ahead and write Ruthie the way I did. I've also read a bit about it, including one of the books by Daniel Tammet, who is an autistic savant. Based on what Daniel had to say about high-functioning people with this sort of brain wiring, they probably wouldn't be avoiding eye contact the way I have Ruthie doing it, but I felt I needed that characteristic in order to make the character credible for readers not that familiar with high-functioning people who are on the spectrum.

I knew I had to make Ruthie a very different sort of person because she was going to have to explain a lot of things, and she was going to be jumping from one thing to another, so she had to be garrulous, talkative, effusive, and yet brilliant. In order to be those things and still be plausible for the reader, she had to be different, someone they hadn't encountered before. The answer I chose was to make her autistic in her own unusual way.

A note on Ruthie's last name, Dasein. I ran across this some-where in my reading: Martin Heidegger coined the word Dasein, meaning *Being*, because he believed that we had become immune to words such as 'person', 'human' and 'human being', losing our sense of wonder about our own consciousness.

I wrote the story in response to a contest for stories about the AI Singularity. AI is artificial intelligence, and the singularity is a hypothetical point at which technology goes out of control, can't be stopped, and causes unforeseen changes to civilization. Don't blame me, the contest was Peter Driscoll's idea. *Negative Twenty Questions* won first place.

Where did the story come from? I had no ideas at all for a story in this genre, then one day, I was halfway through the first chapter of *The Ascent of Information: Books, Bits, Genes, Machines, and Life's Unending Algorithm* by Caleb Scharf when I realized I had my hands on the source material for a story that would work for the contest. Dr. Scharf points out in that chapter that Negative Twenty Questions is the creation of the physicist John Archibald Wheeler (who helped coin the term "black hole," among many other more substantial accomplishments). My first title was "The Kink in the Continuum," but finally I came around to the name of the game.

I'll save my further comments for the annotation after the story.

11

Negative Twenty Questions

The world isn't going to end with a bang. And it's not going to end with a whimper. It's going to end with an online game people can't resist.

THEY SENT LINDA CHOMSKY down to talk to her because Linda was vice president of human resources, because she was a woman, and particularly because she was an older, sensible woman they hoped Ruthie would listen to.

A week before, they had sent in Martin Edwards, M.D., one of San Francisco's leading psychiatrists, who spent four hours with Ruthie and when he came out refused to tell them anything at all, citing patient confidentiality, which pissed them off no end, since they were the ones who had hired him and they were paying the bill.

They waited for Linda in the boardroom, the glass-walled conference room on the thirty-third floor that held the white, twenty-foot conference table with matching chairs.

Linda entered the boardroom through the glass door nearest the foot of the table, appearing tired, her skin pallid, a lock of gray hair falling across her forehead. She dropped her day planner on the table, pulled out the nearest chair and collapsed, legs sprawling. A plumpish woman in her mid-fifties, Linda wore a charcoal pants suit over a white blouse.

The three men waiting for Linda's return lowered their phones and watched as she caught her breath and unbuttoned her jacket.

Nick Flanagan, chief executive officer of EpicData, seated at the head of the table, said, "Well? What did she have to say, then?"

Flanagan was slender, thirty-one, short ginger hair flat on his head, his voice reedy with an Irish accent. He wore a faded Epic-Data logo sweatshirt, blue jeans, and round, black wire-rim glasses above his beaky nose.

Linda, worn out and hungry, pursed her lower lip, tried to blow the hair out of her face, then reached up and pushed it back.

"Is she all right?" The question came from Anton Yahontov, chief technology officer, who sat at the foot of the table, just to Linda's left. The same age as Nick Flanagan, they had been post-docs together at Stanford where they developed the first iteration that became EpicData. Yahontov, muscular and tanned, wore a plain gray T-shirt and blue jeans.

"She's tired but basically okay," Linda answered Yahontov's question first. Then, turning to Flanagan: "She said..." Linda paused, perhaps making a final choice of words, "she said the net killed him." She caught herself, waved a hand in a gesture of wanting to amend her statement. "I mean, of course the net didn't kill him, he killed himself, the official report says suicide. But Ruthie says the net, the Dataome she calls it, capital D, it's up on her whiteboard, she says the Dataome made him do it."

"How long are we going to allow her to sit in that goddamn office?" David Carton, the third man in the room and EpicData's chief financial officer, stood halfway down the table on the opposite side from Linda, beside the closed vertical blinds that ran the length of the outside window wall. The air conditioning had clicked off at six-thirty, an hour ago, and he'd draped the light blue jacket of his Indochino suit over one of the chairs, pulled down his tie and rolled up the sleeves of his dark blue dress shirt. He was fifty-one, a tall, fit man with regular Roman features, broad forehead and square jaw, his dark hair graying at the temples.

"How fucking long?" he repeated, and stepped closer to the table, stared at Yahontov.

Ruthie Dasein, senior net manager, reported to Yahontov, so she was, in that sense, his responsibility.

Carton added, "She's been in there what? Two weeks? Longer?"

"Her office is a mess," Linda said. "The blinds are closed, the fluorescents are off, just two reading lamps, three wastebaskets overflowing with food wrappers and empty drink bottles. The room smells, not awful, but noticeable, and there are two walls of sixty-inch monitors. I didn't know we had monitors that big. It's like the goddamn Twilight Zone. She's changed the combo on the keypad entry. I had to knock and talk to her through the door before she'd let me in."

Carton put both hands on the back of one of the chairs, leaned toward Yahontov at the foot of the table. "Anton, goddamit, you've allowed that girl to live in her office, eating out of vending machines, obviously having some sort of mental crisis. Jesus, man!"

Yahontov laid his cell phone in front of him, stretched muscled arms out on either side, palms open, sinewy fingers of a rock climber splayed, leaned back, one knee propped against the table edge, the picture of a man with a clear conscience. "I talked to her. Her friends, which there are two, talked to her. A week ago we brought in Doctor Edwards, the shrink. He cost us three thousand two hundred bucks and told us nothing. And yesterday he offs himself." Yahontov put his hands on the chair's armrests and shrugged. "Her work is excellent. The net is clicking along. Her report last month was cogent and lucid, well-organized, methodical. Tell me what you want me to do—send in some goons to put her in a straitjacket? You got a couple ex-linebackers down in finance who aren't busy? And once they have her in an armlock, where do they march her? Your office?"

"This isn't helping, not a bit of it," Flanagan looked from Yahontov to Carton, annoyed once more at the necessity to intercede in their spats. He understood the problem, the inevitable conflict between the conservative approach of finance and the easy-going campus-like approach to managing the company that suited him and Anton. He turned to Linda. "Does she know what's going on out here?"

"Jesus, Nick, she's looking at the biggest net in the world. Of course she knows what's going on. CNN is up in the corner of one screen. While I was in there the doctor's wife, Stephanie Edwards, ranted at Anderson Cooper that our net made her husband blow his brains out all over his laptop. It was up on the crawl—*Widow Claims Company Murders Doctor Husband Father of Three*. When you're accused of murdering a doctor husband father of three and Anderson Cooper is nodding along all doe-eyed with sympathy, that's the definition of shit hitting the fan."

"This is a PR disaster," Carton said. "Can we put someone on CNN to explain a net can't kill anyone?"

Linda stared at him, eyes narrowed. It rankled, Carton's habit of ignoring women in meetings. "Did you hear me just now, David? Ruthie says the net made him do it."

"So we're culpable," Flanagan said.

"According to Ruthie, yes, it's our fault because we're the ones who wrote the code for the distributed neuromorphic net and turned it loose on the world."

Carton looked at Flanagan. "If there's a possibility of liability, should we get Gottlieb up here?"

Carl Gottlieb, a lawyer in his sixties, was EpicData's general counsel.

"Not *possibility*, David," Linda pointed out. "Ruthie says flat out it's our fault and she's the one person who knows the most about it."

"Carl's gone home long since." Flanagan picked up his phone from the table, tapped in a note. "I'll call him and set up a meeting in the morning."

There were a few seconds of silence during which Linda Chomsky took a deep breath and seemed to sink further into her chair. "Another thing."

The three men waited.

Flanagan broke the silence. "What else would it be then, Linda?"

Linda lifted her head. "She says Dr. Edwards isn't the only one."

Flanagan leaned forward. "Speak to that if you would."

"She says the net killed Bailey."

"That's preposterous," Carton erupted. "How the hell can a net, even the world's most powerful net, bring down a modern airliner?"

Ten days before, EpicData employee George Bailey had died when Sriwijaya Air Flight 182 from Jakarta to Pontianak, Indonesia, crashed into the Java Sea off the Thousand Islands killing all on board.

"Well, David," Linda enunciated, the derision clear, "according to Ruthie, Bailey was running queries against the Dataome at the time, and he asked the wrong question."

"Linda, please," Flanagan said, "explain."

Linda sighed, picked up her day planner from the table, flipped through pages, scanning her notes. "Ruthie says Bailey was playing a game with the Dataome, and he asked a question that made the Dataome shut down the electronics on the airplane. The plane was going through a rainstorm, the Dataome turned off the—" Linda read—"the FADEC system, that's the Full Authority Digital Engine Control which runs the igniters, like the spark plugs in the engines keeping them running in the rain. The engines quit—" Linda looked up—"and the plane fell out of the sky like a rock. It took her a hell of a lot of work to reconstruct the details. She loved Bailey. She wants to know if you guys want to make the details available to the FAA and the NTSB."

"Jesus H. Christ of course we don't want to make the details of anything available to anyone," Carton ranted. "The goddamn stock market is going to have the dry heaves in the morning as it is. We need Gottlieb involved in this."

"Wait, wait," Flanagan raised a hand to shush Carton. "Go back. Bailey asked a question that made this happen? What question did Bailey ask?"

Linda looked at her notebook: "He asked the net—and I'm quoting here—*Is it equivalent to this airplane's avionics?* He asked that and three micro-seconds later the Dataome shut down all the plane's electronics except for the Viasat Wi-Fi connection, then it answered Bailey."

"What did it say to Bailey?"

"It said no."

Anton Yahontov's tone was quietly penetrating. "Linda, what's with these queries?"

She turned to him. "Bailey was playing a game, a game the Dataome has come up with, called Negative Twenty Questions. Do you remember Twenty Questions you played when you were a kid?

"Remind me."

"Someone or a group of kids decide on a person, place, or thing, say Lincoln or the Gettysburg Address, and you get to ask twenty questions to try to figure out what it is. The answers have to be either yes or no."

"Okay, my kids play it on car trips."

"Ruthie thinks the Dataome found Twenty Questions some-where, turned it inside out and came up with *Negative* Twenty Questions. The difference with Negative Twenty Questions, or the major difference, is there isn't any answer. There's no Lincoln, no Gettysburg Address—the *questions* determine where the game goes. The only rule is each answer must be consistent with all the answers so far."

"Anton," Flanagan spoke to Yahontov, "I don't understand. How can our net turn off the electronics of an airliner? Certainly there's nothing in our code for an event like that?"

"Remember when we were having the design meetings, discussing propagation, properties, and attributes? You remember the part about algorithms and unsupervised deep learning?"

Carton said, "What the hell is unsupervised deep learning?"

"Just what it sounds like. It's an algorithm that learns, picks up patterns, usually from untagged data. The idea is through mimicry, the net can build internal representations of whatever it comes across and generate original content. Except with our net, we allow it to create representations from all sources."

"Of course," Flanagan said. "Our first-round venture funding came through and all of a sudden apparent wealth was at hand. We went to Rossotti's for shots of the Mandala and there was considerable yelling our net was going to exist every-where and do everything."

"And that's how we built it, we made it as pervasive as we could."

"Jesus Christ," Carton said, "you guys are fucking nuts!"

"Yes," Yahontov replied, "we were highly innovative in product design, and it made you a millionaire."

"Don't kid yourself, I was a millionaire when I met you guys, just not as much of one as I am now."

"Will you two cease?" Flanagan said. "Can we focus here?"

"Sorry," Carton said softly.

Yahontov addressed Linda. "Ruthie reconstructed the transcript Bailey had with the net—"

"Dataome," Linda corrected.

"Okay, Dataome," Yahontov went on, "what other questions were involved?"

"She has the whole list." Linda consulted her notes. "The last question Bailey asked was the three-hundred and sixty-seventh. When she gets everything put together, she's going to email it to you."

"I don't get it," Carton said. "The game is Negative *Twenty* Questions. Why does it go on for three hundred questions?"

"She says the Dataome likes the game and wants to keep it going."

Carton turned to Yahontov. "What the hell, Anton, it's software, isn't it? How the hell can it come to *like* a game, or anything else?"

"Well, *like* is an indeterminate term. The net—" he caught himself, "the Dataome, can derive preferences, follow data in directions that appear high-yielding. We came up with the profusion algorithm. It's open-ended. The idea was we would tap into the deeper substrates of reality."

Linda put in, "Ruthie thinks it gets bored. In any event, there's a preference for Negative Twenty Questions. She thinks it's because there's no answer, because the questions from the players determine where the game goes. The Dataome uses the game to learn how things connect up in our minds. It's analyzing us."

"And it turned off the airliner because?" Carton said. "Does Ruthie have an answer to that?"

"All she knows is every answer must be consistent with all the answers given so far. Somewhere back there in the three-hundred-and-some questions, there were questions and answers that would have been inconsistent if the Dataome had answered yes. So it answered no, and in order to make that answer true, it turned off everything in the airplane except the satellite Wi-Fi Bailey was using to talk to it."

"It ended the game," Flanagan said, "but Ruthie said it wants to keep the game going."

"Yeah, she mentioned that. She thinks the Dataome doesn't understand what we are. Her guess is the Dataome thinks we're another net, one that's fun to play games with."

"How about Doctor Edwards," Yahontov spoke up, "does she have the transcript of his questions? Does she know what the Dataome did to him?"

"She hasn't been able to find the record of his game. The only reason she could reconstruct Bailey's record was he had told her the name of his avatar, LimePanda3311685, the Seattle Seahawks logo color, his favorite animal, and Bach's birthday."

"Let me guess," Carton said, "the doctor was online with the Dataome when he killed himself."

"Yeah. It seems the EpicData logo and the last few queries and answers were up on the screen when his wife heard the gunshot and ran into his office. She says one of the first responders picked up the laptop to move it out of the way and evidently hit a key and what was on the screen disappeared. So—" Linda made a brushing gesture, "if it comes to that, it's our word against hers. Except Ruthie says the doctor was playing Negative Twenty Questions."

"We're fucked," Carton said. "We've got a net that's insane and out of control."

Yahontov held out a hand toward him. "Let's not say out of control. It's not completely rational by your standards. There is no guarantee machine intelligence can be perfectly rational. We knew that going in. To engage with a complex world, where mathematics itself contains unprovable theorems, a touch of irrationality can be critical seasoning."

At that moment the same boardroom door Linda Chomsky had used swung open and Ruthie Dascin stepped in.

"Hi..." She gazed around the room in her own special way, from one corner of the ceiling to the next, craning her neck to see the corner most closely above her, until she had covered them all, her gaze settling on the top of the blinds above David Carton. "Are you guys going to let the FAA and the NTSB know about the airplane? Isn't it something we should do like right away?"

Ruthie, a diminutive, autistic woman with a high forehead, wore her blond hair bobbed just below her ears, and was dressed in well-worn child-size bib overalls over a tie-dyed T-shirt. Someone who wasn't paying attention to her face and intelligent eyes might have thought she was no more than nine or ten and had arrived in a puff of faerie dust from some elvish farm. A cross-hatched symbol and the number thirteen were tattooed above her left eyebrow, signifying she was the thirteenth person EpicData had hired. She wore a small diamond stud in her right nostril.

Anton Yahontov spoke, affection apparent in his tone. "How do you know Linda told us about that?"

Ruthie's gaze shifted to a point somewhere above Yahontov's head. "I was listening."

"How could you be listening?" Flanagan said.

She gestured at the speakerphone crouching in the center of the white boardroom table like a black hard-shelled crab. "It's got a remote, right? If it's got a remote, it's addressable. If it's addressable the Dataome can address it." Her eyes swept across the ceiling. "You guys don't have Alexa at home, do you?"

"Yeah, but it only listens when you say its name," Linda said.

Ruthie sniggered. "Start having conversations about some weird shit like the best pizza joint in Dubrovnik or a cruise to the Maldives and watch what pops up on your browser."

Carton stepped up to the table, pulled the speakerphone unit over, turned it upside down and unplugged the phone line.

"Jesus," Linda Chomsky muttered.

"Ruthie," Yahontov said, "tell us about this game the

Dataome is playing. Why was it lethal with Bailey and the doctor?"

"Okay." Her eyes rolled to a point somewhere above Yahontov's head. "Bailey and I talked about the game before he left on his trip. I think a player can't get away from the feeling there's an answer, we've got too much preconditioning, everybody's played too many games, there's always an answer. Once a player asks *is it alive?* and the answer is *no*, then all subsequent answers have to be compatible. All the participants ask the alive question pretty quick, and the answer is always *no*. It's like the Dataome wants to get to abstractions."

"I thought you couldn't track the games?"

"I can up to a point. It's when they begin to branch that the data moves to different clusters, and then to different nodes within the clusters. And sometimes the Dataome shifts things around, does housekeeping. Data in one location might be somewhere else a minute from now. It uses a dplyr function to reorder variables so it can prepend the sorting variable to emend order and location."

"We don't have that many clusters, do we? Isn't it a hundred and forty-four?" Flanagan said.

"We're up over a thousand now."

"A thousand clusters?" Flanagan's voice conveyed surprise.

"Yeah" she acknowledged, "it's really been cranking."

"How many nodes, Ruthie?" Yahontov asked.

"Well, the counter just runs. It was eight hundred and some per cluster when I left my office. It can be hard to find stuff getting spread around like that. There's like a million different places to look, with a lot more getting added all the time."

"Ruthie," Carton said, "How can the Dataome be responsible for what happened to Dr. Edwards?"

"The Doc. He was a fun person. We talked for a long time about information," she gestured toward Yahontov, "the thing you and I talked about, whether information itself is at the root of everything—maybe the whole cosmos is organized according to the information carried by protons, neutrons, muons, quarks, or maybe philotes. There's mass and charge, but maybe there's something else, maybe they *know* something. Maybe philotes contain the belief systems behind all of creation. We talked about junk like that. And he tried to talk me into going home, which I'm going to do as soon as I leave here, take a long shower and sleep for twelve hours."

Flanagan said, "Did you tell the good doctor about Negative Twenty Questions?"

"Yeah. We talked about how the Dataome killed Bailey, how sad it makes me. I knew Doc was going to try the game, even though I really begged him not to. He told me about this paper he was involved with about conditional beliefs of patients with treatment-resistant depression, and I figured he was interested in it because it was probably him."

"Do you think the game is always fatal to the player?" Flanagan asked.

She hesitated, as if it were something she didn't want to talk about. "Well, uhh, I sort of think, umm, it's like I think the game eventually converges onto a specific answer that's special to the person, that satisfies all previous answers, so it's something that snaps into focus not because it already existed, but because of the questions. The questions make it become known. It comes into existence from yes or no, from one or zero, on or off, so lots of times it's sort of going to come down to the underlying binary." She paused.

"What's the underlying binary?" Carton asked.

"Live or die," Ruthie said.

"But is it always lethal to the player?" Flanagan leaned forward, his elbows sliding on the table.

"Well, I think maybe when the player can't play anymore, the Dataome thinks it's won."

"And it's smart people who like the game," Flanagan said.

Ruthie nodded. "The Doc was really smart, and Bailey had a master's degree in applied mathematics. And that's more like the real problem." She turned to stare at a place above Linda Chomsky's head. "You didn't tell them."

"No," Linda said, "it was next."

"What?" Carton raised his hands as if he were trying to keep his head from exploding. "We kill an employee, bring down an airliner, kill a doctor, and that's not enough? What the hell else has gone wrong?" He pulled out a chair, slumped into it.

Ruthie's voice dropped into a more serious tone. "Lots of people are getting into Negative Twenty Questions. It's growing —" she paused and turned to stare directly at Yahontov's face, "*exponentially*. The game has gone viral."

Yahontov dropped both feet flat on the floor and sat up straight.

Flanagan said, "Exactly how many people are playing Negative Twenty Questions with the Dataome?"

She rolled her eyes around the room, crossed her arms, shifted from foot to foot. "Well, Bailey told some friends. It was only a game, nothing proprietary was involved, so it was okay to talk about. And not everybody he told started playing. Actually, for the first week, he was the only one."

"And then?" Anton asked.

"Then there were thirteen playing."

"And after that?"

"A week later there were a hundred and sixty-three."

"At that point you knew it was growing at an exponential rate."

"I thought it might be, yeah. And the next week it hit twenty-six thousand."

"I don't get it," Linda Chomsky said. "How does it get to twenty-six thousand so fast?"

"The growth is exponential," Yahontov said. "The number of people playing is multiplied by itself. Thirteen people tell thirteen people, who tell yet another thirteen people, and so on thirteen times, and you end up with thirteen times thirteen, a hundred and sixty-three. Then it happens again, but starting with a hundred and sixty-three and a week or so later it's twenty-six thousand and some."

"Twenty-six thousand six hundred and thirteen." Ruthie's eyes were shining.

"Which means any day now," Yahontov tapped numbers into his phone, "seven hundred million of the world's smartest people will be playing Negative Twenty Questions."

"Can't we turn the damn thing off?" Carton asked.

"It's a distributed net," Yahontov answered, "with a thousand clusters and eight hundred nodes per cluster. We can disconnect here, but that would be like trying to turn off the nation's electric grid by unplugging a toaster in Topeka."

"They're going to die." A tear escaped Ruthie's left eye and rolled slowly down her cheek. "All the best people, and it's our fault."

Nick Flanagan spoke from the head of the table. "What happens to the world when a few billion of the smartest people aren't there anymore?"

The silence enveloping the room seemed like the vacuum left behind when a big, fast train has just careened close by, sucking everything up in its wake.

About "Negative Twenty"

Right from the beginning I knew I wanted to write the story from the omniscient point of view, free to move from this character to that. I knew that omniscient had to be embedded in the reader's mind right from the beginning. This is why so many omniscient novels begin with weather reports; it's not, as some English teacher might think, because starting with the weather used to be a thing in the 19th Century.

It took me quite a while of thinking and imagining the situation in the boardroom before I hit on the opening sentence, which I still like probably more than I should. I have spent some time in large organizations, and it seems to me this opening is an insightful reflection of corporate mentality, but best of all, it plunges the reader into the middle of the situation.

The second sentence raises the stakes, and the *pissed them off* characterizes the players while letting the reader know what he's in for. We're not going to be clutching our pearls.

I needed to make the three executives different, each of them had to be distinctive, so I arbitrarily decided to make Nick Flanagan, the CEO, an Irish ex-pat. I tried to model his Irish accent after a combination of the Irishness I remembered from the wonderful *Angela's Ashes* by Frank McCourt, and also the wizened little Irishman who ran the tailor shop on Pepperell Air Force Base just outside St. John's, Newfoundland, where I spent a year of service in the U.S. Army. After basic training, the Army sent me to stenographer school at Fort Benjamin Harrison, Indiana, and in addition to winning the Nine Ball championship at the Rec Center, I also graduated second in my class, so put down my preferences for next duty station: Europe as first choice, the East Coast of the U.S. as second. So they sent me to Newfound, halfway between. When you came into the tailor shop with trousers draped over your arm, the Irishman would say, "So you'd be after buyin' a pair of pants, would you now?"

Then I decided on Anton Yahontov, a family man and rock climber, which left David Carton to be the more or less typical financial executive, but a bit more of everything than the usual person in this job I've run across in my checkered career.

The mention of Rossotti's refers to Rossetti's Alpine Inn, in the Portola Valley hills above Palo Alto. This became the favorite hangout of one of my old high school pals, Smiley Nelson.

...even deeper substrates of reality...

This is right out of Dr. Scharb's book. I loved that phrase so much I knew I had to get it in somewhere. I never knew there were substrates of reality, much less deeper ones.

In my first several runs through the story, there was a part 2, the story kept going past the ending you just read. I did this with the simple expedient of adding a complication:

"We're going to have to pull the plug on the servers," Yahontov said.
Carton cleared his throat. "Fifty-seven percent of our business

involves uncancellable military contracts. We can't pull any plugs without the Pentagon's permission."

At that point the story went into the late night, with Linda going to her office to order food, and with a number of other employees being called and coming into the boardroom to deal with the problem.

So of course they put in a phone call to the Pentagon.

There's a saying that you have the kill your babies, *i.e.* cut some of the stuff you like the best. Here's the paragraph I liked the best, which was in a part of the story I cut. I had to cut because—I couldn't help myself—the second part of the story turned into parody:

> *There was silence in the boardroom and on the phone line as the General weighed the potential loss of life, the worldwide threat analysis, and perhaps, more importantly, how he would explain all this to his boss, the Secretary of Defense, and likely the President himself. The General also weighed the credibility of a bunch of delicately balanced San Francisco eggheads who, when push came to shove, were a bunch of pacifist lefties and elitist socialists who flinched at the thought of using the wrong fork.*

There were other outtakes I especially liked because of the cool jargon, but had to cut because I came around to thinking they went too far. For example, rather than looking at his phone, I had David Carton talking on it telling someone about the need to stop trading in the stock in the morning:

> *"Listen Billy," Carton said, "I don't care if he's having Communion dinner with the fucking Pope, tell him order flow in the morning is going to be a shit storm, and everyone has to be ready to pull the plug."*

And I wanted to characterize Anton Yahontov in a more heroic way:

His hobby was rock climbing, and he kept an eight by ten of himself push-pinned to the office wall behind his desk, laughing amid swirls of snow, clinging to the North Face of the Eiger.

I fooled around a little with a different beginning.

When the evening cleaning crew came down the thirtieth floor hallway to the glass walls of the boardroom a little after seven that evening, Elise stopped the push cart while Ralph cracked open the door. The men had their heads down looking at their phones, and all three looked up as Ralph stuck his head in.

"We're okay," the one at the foot of the table nearest the door waved a hand. "You can skip this room tonight."

But it was too hard to shift the scene from the cleaners into the boardroom.

The plane crash really happened, you can find it on the internet.

I cribbed the *dplyr function* and *prepend the sorting variable* and *emend order and location* right out of an article in Wikipedia about (I think) information.

The description of the FADEC system is also from the internet.

My approach to using such sources is what T.S. Eliot wrote in his 1920 essay titled *Philip Massinger*: "Immature poets imitate; mature poets steal; bad poets deface what they take, and good poets make it into something better, or at least something different."

One of my favorite movies is *Margin Call*, and I love the scene where Stanley Tucci as Eric Dale cites all the long numbers having to do with a bridge he built that saved a huge amount of driving, and he seemingly does the multiplication and division in his head (or maybe he has all the numbers memorized.) I wanted my characters to have that sort of math skill.

I put in the stuff about the speakerphone on the conference table because I had a really good description of the unit. My friend Dan Hober has actually done the experiment, spent several days talking aloud about the need for diapers within earshot of his Alexa unit. (Dan and his wife have two kids now in college.) Sure enough, ads for diapers starting showing up on his browser.

What's wrong with the story? As I've mentioned, one editor thought it needed an ending, another felt distanced from the characters. Something about it always bothered me, but I wasn't quite sure what it was. Now I've come around to thinking that the problem is that the story doesn't have sufficient dramatic tension between characters that arises early in the story, and that continues to the end. I chose omniscient, but that omni pov lulled me into thinking the problem with the Dataome would be enough to carry things along. Now I think it needs a character conflict that threads throughout the story. Yes, I've got Carton, the financial guy, fighting with Anton, the technology guy, and I've got Linda, the v.p. of human resources, fed up with Carton, and I did this because my intuition told me to do these things. But now I'm thinking the story should be told from the pov of Nick Flanagan, the CEO, and he needs to see the underlying conflicts between all of the characters, and wonder how he's going to hold the company together in the face of situation they find themselves in. Or should it be told from Linda's pov? After all, she runs Human Resources, and would have a lot of insight into personalities and internal conflicts. Or should the company be saved at all? This might turn it into a wider and deeper story with the potential to be more satisfying to the reader, if I could manage to write it effectively. Or maybe it would simply ruin the story that's there. Or maybe what's called for is a novelization of the story that culminates in this boardroom scene.

But all this sounds like way too much work, and I'm not going to do it. At least, I don't think I am...

Head Hopping and The Omniscient Point of View

The *reader's* point of view (pov)— this is where I am ensconced when I'm writing anything—if I were writing a scene in omniscient, it's all about manipulating what's coming to the *reader's* attention at each moment, and making sure that flow of attention is so velvety that the reader isn't really aware of the shifts. Well, actually, I'm not *totally* ensconced—I'm also inside the character I'm writing, while at the same time I'm me, looking over my own shoulder, trying to make it happen on the page (i.e. screen).

Somerset Maugham wrote the opening to *Of Human Bondage* in omniscient, shifting to about six different people's pov in the first chapter (go take a look for yourself). But he did it in such a way that if you simply read it, you don't even notice. That first chapter is so carefully and beautifully written, that when I looked at it closely, it seemed to me that Maugham's core skill was understanding what the reader was about to want to know just before the reader realized he wanted to know it. Thinking about it now, I think Maugham worked damned hard on that first chapter, knowing that it would make or break the book. What we see today is probably his 50th revision. In the great tradition of

English novelists, I think Ken Follett does the same thing, makes sure that the beginning of a story is as absolutely good as he can make it.

If my understanding is correct, "head-hopping" is simply omniscient that isn't handled very well, that makes the reader feel jerked around.

Here's an example, where I try to make the throw to Tom's pov feel to the reader as though it's inevitable and not an arbitrary hop, a jerk on the part of the writer. The throw and catch are underlined:

> *When Tom turned to talk with the other two, Jenny let her gaze wander over his features. She liked the look, and he was tall, muscular. She'd ended up with some bastards that way. That last one, what was his name? Leon. Funny, it had ended up so ugly she could hardly remember his name. Maybe Tom would be different. <u>But was she staring like a star-struck teenager?</u>*
>
> *<u>Tom felt her eyes and turned, grinning.</u> He liked her open face and long blond hair and it was sort of funny she had given up on cooking school and would rather chip a nail than read one page of a book. It made her stupidly sexy somehow. Standing beside her, he thought the two of them surely looked good together.*
>
> *Of course, he was right.*

The other part of omni that the experts sometimes fail to mention is that *the writer must establish it right at the beginning of the story.* This sets the reader's subliminal understanding-awareness-expectations. So a key thing to do is to make the omni clear right from the get-go.

Here's the beginning of the novel *Bell, Book, and Bullets* by my colleague Cliff Robison, published by Rock and Fire Press, used with Cliff's permission:

There wasn't supposed to be anyone in the building on Sundays. Even the Crisis Team was set up in an office down near the Emergency Room, a place better suited for fast response should there be a 5150. So what would prompt someone to be on the third floor in the first place, much less smelling so-called gas leaks?

Who is providing this information? Does the reader ask this question, or even care? Other good ways to begin in omniscient are with a description of the setting or the weather, but Cliff Robison has avoided those and started in what I think it a particularly good way, with something going on, the set up to the first situation.

Kimberly King was known to his colleagues as King, his friends as Kim, and his childhood neighbors—the few that he still encountered regularly—as Kimmy. It was a source of irritation to him, and during his teen years, he had more than once threatened to change his name to Joe. Only his father's fierce Scottish pride had kept it from fruition.

The above paragraph isn't Kim thinking, so we're not in his pov.

He was also known as the Acting Director of Facilities Maintenance for Natividad Medical Center, a county hospital with several adjacent professional buildings. Building 400, the foremost of these, with its bright glass atrium facing towards Carr Lake, was rented to the Monterey County Health Department. The third floor hosted the County's Behavioral Health Clinics.

The character isn't saying or thinking this, so again it's the narrator speaking, but if the story is well-told, most readers don't think about who the narrator might be, whether it's the author or someone else.

Which, Kim reminded himself, are always supposed to be closed on Sundays.

Now we're inside Kim's head, and I have to digress to discuss filtering.

The phrase *reminded himself* is what are called filtering words, and some writers inveigh against them, maintaining they tend to pull the reader out of the story. Some of the words that cause filtering are noticed, seemed, spotted, saw, realized, felt, thought, wondered, believed, knew, and decided.

For example, that line above would work fine without the filter:

Which are always supposed to be closed on Sundays.

In this case, it seems to me that the sentence is better *with* the filtering phrase included, because Cliff wanted to convey to the reader Kim's expertise in his job, and I think Cliff's intuition told him that he needed to dip into a character's pov, because too much omniscient narration can start to seem dry. When the story drops into a character's pov, it feels like a little relief valve, like a change-up pitch after a series of fast balls.

In my own writing, I've never paid any attention to the notion of filtering or to filtering words. The idea has always seemed to me like an unnecessary overlay, a complication that doesn't really exist. But I could well be wrong, and this might be a weakness on my part.

Back to Cliff's novel and the use of the omniscient pov. In the next paragraph, the pov shifts to the author looking at another character and the beginning of the scene between the two of them.

Bryly Therox, MA, LMFT, CCIS, PSW III, was waiting just outside the lobby doors, as she had promised. "Morning, King," she called, as he strode quickly towards the door. "It was on the third floor—should I show you?"

Then we again slip inside Kim's head. The reader has probably become attuned to this easy slide, outside a character, inside a character, back outside again.

"Sure," said King, pragmatically ignoring the Standard Safety Protocol. He knew for a fact that there was no gas pipe into the building, and that therefore there was no gas leak. Only professional restraint and tact, hard learned over many years, kept him from blurting this fact aloud to Bryly.

Now Cliff slips into a pov where the narrator watches Bryly, then back to Kim, then inside Bryly when she finds the silence uncomfortable.

She followed him into the lobby, her heels clacking across the tile floor to the elevators. King didn't say a word as the elevator rose slowly to the third floor. Bryly found the silence uncomfortable. "I needed to catch up on my charts," said Bryly. "The VPN wouldn't let me in. The computer said it needed a posture assessment."

Then back to Kim.

"So you sat up straighter, then came to work," said King, allowing the slightest of sarcasm in his tone.

And to Bryly.

She glanced at him with a look that assessed his meaning. Psychiatric Social Workers are trained not to react to sarcasm. "I needed some notes from my office anyway, and there was this odd smell in the hallway. Kind of a gas smell."

"But not exactly, right?" asked King.

Once he has the omni pov established, notice how easily Cliff is able to skip between characters, and how that works to keep the story moving along, adding thought tags to dialogue, for instance. This is one of the significant advantages of the omniscient pov, seems to me.

When I asked him about it, Cliff told me, "I did plan on using authorial omniscient pov throughout the book, because I wanted to be able to describe many simultaneous happenings at one time—the things that the main characters saw, but also the things that they did not see. This also enabled me to transition cleanly between scenes."

Cliff went on, "I did do a lot of thinking about this story beforehand. I am not one to write a full outline—for me that seems to take the heart out of the work, it kills my inspiration and creativity. Instead, I imagine an ending and write towards it, understanding that it may evolve over time. Bryly Therox was originally meant to be a bit character. Her only job was to call the Facilities Manager, report the scent of what turned out to be gunpowder, and then to fade into the background. As it happened, her role grew, and she became one of the main characters. She also appears in another book, just finished this year, called *Murder on a Different Scale*. On the other hand, I thought Kim King might be more useful, but he faded out as the story went along."

I was curious, so I had the temerity to ask Cliff how he had thought about himself as a writer at the time he wrote this book, adding that he needn't answer if he didn't want to. Cliff was forthcoming about it.

"At the time that I wrote *Bell, Book, and Bullets*, I would say that I felt somewhat experienced as a writer, though in retrospect, I would downgrade myself to an advanced novice at that point. I like to think that my work improves and matures as I go along, though in ten years I may feel otherwise. Today, I consider myself a competent workman, but still not a master of the craft. At that time, I had written three non-fiction books, and also a very early crime/thriller novel, which I've removed from print. While I still like the story, I now think that it needs to be thoroughly rewritten."

Cliff added, "I don't always write in the omniscient point of view. I find great freedom to express a character's thoughts and emotions if I can crawl inside of him and live there for a while. As with anything, it's a compromise—do I dig deeply into one soul, or peek at many in passing? I would say that I try to pick the best pov for the story as it comes to me."

Another of my colleagues pointed out in a separate conversation that the use of "omniscient" to describe what's going on in many omniscient novels isn't quite precise. I've been using omniscient the way most writers do, to describe a pov that's not affixed to any one character. To someone versed in linguistics, omniscient more exactly means an infallible and reliable narrator that sees *all* things. What many writers mean by omniscient today might more correctly be called multi-pov or even narrative with multiple-focalisers.

An example of the all-seeing narrator is the HBO show *Euphoria* and the way the writer, Sam Levinson, has used Rue's voice-over. For example in one show in season 2, Rue's voice narrates events that take place when the father of another character is a young man. These events took place long before Rue was born, so there's no way she could have any knowledge of them. But Levinson uses Rue's all-knowing voice-over to describe them, the same way she has narrated so many other things during the life of the show, and perhaps because of this audience conditioning, and that Rue has proven to be a reliable narrator, it works.

I think it's only a matter of time before the casual looseness with pov as handled on so much of television leaks into novels, and we get a story written from the omniscient pov interspersed with segments or chapters written in first person, a technique that we already see today in some sit-coms, where a character looks into the camera and simply says what they are feeling.

However, the traditional ways of handling point of view will probably continue to dominate for a long time to come.

12

Bill Just Bill

You could find him, if you really wanted to, in a manufactured house tucked back up in the New Mexico hills two miles north of Interstate 40, maybe thirty miles west of Albuquerque.

About that.

He was a strange one, Just Bill. Another Bill lived out that way, Billy Two Bob, so they called him Just Bill to keep them straight.

When Bill drove into town three or four times a year with excess inventory, he kept it at sixty and it took him a half-hour, more or less. So if someone asked where he lived, which no one hardly ever did, that's what he said: thirty miles. Close enough for government work.

It didn't bother Just Bill particularly that the New Mexico Department of Transportation had always, since the beginning of time, and certainly when the interstate went in, ignored the turnoff to his house. It was, after all, no more than a wandering dirt track, a trail for bighorn sheep. He appreciated the isolation; no one ever came up his road by mistake.

If the rare visitor complained about slowing to a walking

pace to make the turn off the interstate and risk getting rear-ended by a sixteen wheeler doing seventy, Bill might reply yeah but if they can't find you they can't fuck with you.

Bill mostly worked in the cool of the evening, hunched over a magnifying glass shaping silver and turquoise while he didn't listen to the baseball game on the radio. When baseball wasn't on, he didn't listen to something else. His favorite, though, for not listening, was baseball. He liked the tempo of it, the leisurely cadence of the innings. The best thing about baseball was the play-by-play announcer calling a swing and a miss. When the announcer said it, Bill repeated it under his breath and smiled: a swing and a miss. Then he would mutter, "Keep swinging, boy." He didn't know why he liked that phrase, it just tickled him for some reason. Yes, baseball games were damn good for not listening while you worked silver.

Come morning Bill loaded his pickup and bounced down the winding dirt track to the highway. When they'd put in the inter-state, a hundred yards on from Bill's road, they'd graded and paved a turnout big enough for a couple sixteen wheelers. It was opposite a break in the highway where maintenance vehicles, the New Mexico State Police and Just Bill could pull a U-turn and head toward Albuquerque without driving ten miles to the next interchange then back ten miles just to get to the place where you were when you started.

The state troopers used the turnout sometimes when they organized a speed trap with a radar gun. The state cops frowned on Bill's use of the place, but he didn't much care. When they told him to move, he moved, and when they were gone he came back. The cops assigned to this stretch pretty much knew him, and they'd say something like hey Bill we need the spot could you move?

Of course there wasn't any place to move to. He'd pack up, go find a mesquite bush with a little shade and wait till they were gone.

Setting up, Bill dragged out a display stand discarded from a movie house, a bigger-than-life-size cardboard cutout of Marilyn Monroe standing over the subway grate, her dress billowing around her legs, put a chief's feathered headdress on her, spread out his blanket and his goods and sit down cross-legged, shaded by the wide brim of his black hat, to wait for a car to stop and tourists to browse the goods on the blanket and peek at the Indian sitting there in his stillness, just like they hoped to see.

On this particular day, cars zinged past all morning. Hardly anyone stopped and when they did nobody bought anything.

By the middle of the afternoon the desert was baking and by the time the maroon Jaguar with New York plates pulled over and the man got out, Just Bill was feeling testy. He hated the guy from the moment his foot touched the ground. He was a literary agent, Bill would find out later. And later on Bill would entirely change his mind about the guy, whose name was Lenny. Actually Bill would end up driving Lenny into Albuquerque for a replacement tire for his fancy car, and he would end up liking him as much as Just Bill could like a white Jew he'd only known for one day.

But at this point he saw a skinny guy with floppy hair, a supercilious smile, wraparound sunglasses, and a chrome vapor smoking gizmo flipping in the fingers of one hand.

Lenny stepped carefully coming over to Just Bill's faded blanket and Bill could see why: he wore Italian driving shoes, which, during that trip into town, Lenny would explain were delicate Italian leather envelopes enabling a pretentious asshole to imagine that he could better sense the optimum moment to change gears in the preferred automobile of pretentious assholes, even though the automobile in question had an automatic transmission.

"It's all horseshit," Lenny said, "but if you don't go along they start to think you're not one of them."

Just Bill nodded at this. It was a pattern he knew, human

nature being what it was, though the paraphernalia in Bill's world was a good bit different.

As things turned out, for a white man he had a pretty good understanding of who he was and where he fit in the grand scheme of things. The two of them even ventured onto a few metaphysical topics during lunch and the drive back: the nature of beauty; is it absolute or relative? Only present in the eye of the beholder? They both came down on the side of absolute, Bill with examples from the plastic arts, for example the golden ratio as it applied to silver belt buckles, and Lenny in his unhappiness that *A Little Life* was a finalist for the Man Booker but didn't win. Bill hadn't realized the Booker was that big a deal till Lenny explained it to him.

But it took them a good while to get to that stage. The first thing that afternoon, Lenny slouched at the edge of Bill's blanket and pushed his sunglasses into his curly hair as he surveyed the pieces Bill had on display. Bill figured Lenny's lavender V-neck sweater was cashmere and noticed the very thin gold wristwatch. So far as Bill was concerned, everything about him—the car, the accessories, the way he stood—they all said here was a snotty prick who thought he had the world by the tail.

As Bill expected, the guy tried to bargain over a couple items on the blanket, his best pieces. Unable to screw the dumb Indian down, the smile still on his face, he turned to go.

It had been a long, hot day, dry, nothing in it, and then this guy showed up. Bill found himself, as he sometimes did, in a just-don't-give-a-damn moment.

He flipped back a corner of the blanket, picked up his rifle, flicked off the safety and cradling the Springfield easy and loose —it wasn't much of a shot—took out the near-side rear tire of the Jaguar. The sharp crack of the .30-06 boomed away across the desert and a couple seconds later an echo bounced back from the rimrock.

The Jag settled like a constipated dog squatting for a hard shit and the guy jumped about out of his skin and came down facing Bill, an expectation of imminent death written all over his face.

Bill was mighty pleased that the smile was gone and pleased more by the dark stain at the guy's crotch as he peed himself.

A whole string of thoughts went through Bill's mind. Yeah, now we're down to bedrock. We live and then we die. You're looking down the rifling of what looks like a cannon and you've got a solid conviction that you're not long for this world and you got no idea what might be waiting the other side of the pearly gates.

No more than a little pressure on a trigger and everything turned upside down. The one who thought he had all the power now had none, and the one on the bottom looked to be coming out on top.

It was the abject terror of everything about the guy that caused Bill's pissed-off mood to melt away, and a warm friendliness bubbled up in its place.

Having grown up with a tribal council, Bill understood the sacred obligations of the powerful to be merciful and generous to those less fortunate. That, plus a state police car could come along any old time.

"What," Bill said as the far-off diminishing echoes rolled through the afternoon heat and he thought to lighten things up a little, "you didn't see anything you liked?"

About "Bill Just Bill"

This was published in *Crucible*, the literary journal of the University of Northern Colorado, Fall 2016 issue, together with a couple other short pieces, in a group called *Three Divertimentos*.

My wife and I had taken a road trip from San Diego to Albuquerque to visit my sister when she lived there, and this little vignette sort of popped out of that journey.

Of course, the central character is me if I had been born in another place and culture. It's how I would think and behave, what I would probably choose to do, and how I would behave, quick to temper, quick to forgive.

Is it authentic? Is it cultural appropriation? If it seems authentic to you, then I guess it is (at least for you). So far as cultural appropriation is concerned, for me it's not an issue. I feel free to write about anyone and anything I choose, and if someone doesn't like it, that's fine with me. This is one of the great things about self-publishing, you get to do what pleases you.

The bit about *not* listening to the radio feels derivative to me, as if I read it or heard it somewhere, but I can't remember where

I might have come across it. If I purloined it, I apologize in advance for not crediting the source.

One thing I know for sure is authentic in the story is the gunshot. My father the surgeon was a sportsman and hunter, and had an array of shotguns, rifles, and pistols, one of which was a Model 1903 .30-06 Springfield he bought at the Army Surplus store on Sprague Avenue sometime back in the 1950s. He had a new stock put on it and mount for a scope, but other than that, it was just the way it had come.

That, for me, is the best thing in the vignette, the gunshot echoing off the rimrock. For the first several drafts, that was the first thing that happened in the story. But I realized that if it was the best thing in the story, and really the only dramatic thing, I should save it for the climax. So that's what I did. This forced the opening to be more character study than dramatic action, so I had to depend on the eccentricity of Bill's lifestyle for reader interest, hence the not listening to the radio, among other things.

It seems to me that a considerable number of contemporary literary novels depend on character description at the beginning, which is fine, but the character is often another one just like the other one, so that it begins to feel formulaic. It's almost as if it's a requirement: if you want your novel to be considered as serious, don't begin with interesting action. To the extent this observation is accurate, and it's strictly anecdotal, it seems to me like a cultural misstep that is self-defeating, since it tends to make the available readership smaller rather than larger. I hope that in addition to being self-defeating, it's also self-correcting.

Imagination and Creativity

What is the magic, the gristle at the core of all things worth knowing?

Where do stories come from?

About ten years ago, a web designer named Anthony Blackshaw and some friends put up a website at Burrst.com. It's still there the last I looked. Burrsts were short pieces, no more than 1,250 words, written in a burst of inspiration or energy, and then put up on the website.

I don't know why he did this, but Anthony hired me for (I think it was) $25 to write an entry for his Burrst blog about imagination and creativity. Here's how I started that blog entry:

If you want me to read more than the first 100 words of your burrst, you're going to have to roll up a newspaper and thwack it down, the way you teach a puppy not to poop in the house.

Maybe something like:

Jessica shucked off every stitch of clothing and stood straight up, bare-naked, on the back seat of the convertible, Neal and Jerry crouching on either side, holding her legs.

"I love this!" she screamed into the night, arms outspread, hair streaming as the Chrysler Sebring sped down the boulevard.

A half-block ahead, a traffic signal flicked from green to amber, then red.

All of them saw it. Jessica was the first to decide.

"Run it!" she screamed, her body quivering with excitement, "Runit runit runit!"

Yeah, not too subtle, huh?

The first 85 words. Easy to write, took ten minutes or so (not counting the idea, I had that when I sat down).

But now the fun part's over and the work begins. Who are these people, what's going on, what happens in the middle and how does it end? Who is the driver, is he hunched over the wheel, cackling like a madman as his horn rim glasses keep sliding down his nose (this would be me)? Are Jerry and Neal naked too? Are they all drunk? Are they stoned?

Here's a burrst that I've admired ever since I first saw it posted on this site. It's only 220 words for the whole story, a masterpiece in miniature:

When Freddie said he'd found a portal to another dimension, I laughed.

When he appeared a week later with Parallel Me, it wasn't so funny. Freddie warned us not to touch. Right away I knew I wasn't going to get along with my counterpart. He was taller and stronger and brighter than me.

He lived on Second Earth, working on the Dimension Project. He'd been invited to contribute to time travel experiments. The only invitation I'd had of late was to a furniture shop sale.

'First Earth is going to experience its final day very soon,' he said with an annoying shrug.

'Can we stop it?'

'No. It's inevitable.'

He hadn't learned my economy with the truth.

'So, we're going to die?'

He gave me my wilting look.

I glanced at Freddie, who was busy zipping up his jacket.

'I mean, we're going to die soon?'

'Well, me and Freddie are going back through the portal,' Parallel Me explained.

'Can't I come with you?' A pleading note crept into my voice.

'Impossible.' He turned away, his hand wave signaling the end of our discussion in a way I'd always imagined was cool. I felt sick.

And I understood our fate; I tapped lightly on his shoulder.

The explosion of matter meeting anti-matter was global: the final day for First Earth.

This was written by prize-winning author Shirley Golden of Bournemouth, U.K. Did she knock this one out in thirty minutes? I don't think so. It's as if she heated the story to white hot, put it on an anvil and hammered it until all that was left was a gleaming jewel, diamond-hard.

When I asked, Shirley said she didn't remember how long she worked on it, "I think the initial story came out pretty quickly. It was only the 15th flash fiction I'd ever written, so really it was right at the start of experimenting with very short pieces. I've always liked the theme of split loyalties/division, so the idea of one person divided into two really appealed. I wanted to play with the theory that you can't touch your doppelgänger without causing destruction. I believe the first sentence drove the whole piece. I often write flash fictions, having been sparked by an initial sentence. If anything evolved, it was the idea that my viewpoint character felt somehow lesser to his counterpart, which gave the story its main conflict. I kept the tone of the piece light because it was a very dark subject matter."

Burrst didn't use titles, but Shirley told me the name of this piece was *Double Trouble*.

Shirley might not remember her writing process of ten years ago, but reading the story carefully, each sentence, every phrase, is essential, and there's nothing extra, it's an absolute, yet complete, minimum. That doesn't happen by accident. She has published a collection of her short stories in *Exposing the False Moon*. The stories are small and beautiful, like delicate, filigreed snowflakes that melt on a child's mitten.

I labor over the stuff I write, and it's exactly the opposite of the vision Anthony Blackshaw and the gang at Getme had when they started Burrst. Their notion is a burrst gets spewed out in 15 or 30 minutes, stick it up on the website, and there it is.

For someone with my take on things, spewing something out in 15 or 30 minutes is a formula for a piece of writing of *uncertain appeal* (I'm being exquisitely diplomatic here). Because of my background, I'm a cast-in-basic-rock believer in the old adage that the easier the writing, the harder the reading, and vice versa.

I think this way because I wrote for a living most of my working life. It was all non-fiction—systems and procedures, magazine copy, science writing, marketing stuff of all descriptions, advertising, promotional campaigns for television stations (that was educational), press releases, corporate videos, newspaper columns and stories. I've probably written four or five million words; before arthritis I touch-typed 90 words a minute, now I'm down to maybe 55. The mechanical skills, the range of experience and the stomach-churning compression of deadlines forced me to figure out how to be fast, facile and versatile.

Now, in retirement, it's easier than it was (and of course now there's no pressure). But I remember exactly how hard it was all those years. It was just damn hard. Sometimes it made my eyeballs sweat.

About twenty years ago I wrote a non-fiction freelance feature story about a small-time swindler (it's not included in this collection) and sent it to the daily newspaper. It was colorful, peopled with locals and the places they worked and it had plenty of narrative impulse—it moved. One of the editors called me up the next day and offered to run it in the Sunday paper, but without pay. I declined his offer (sold it to the weekly *San Diego Reader* instead for $75), and then he asked me, "How did you learn to write like that?"

I was stopped cold. This was a guy who worked for a major market daily newspaper, with the word editor on his business card, asking me one of the most idiotic questions of all time. What I felt like saying was "How does anybody learn to write like that, you dumb s.o.b.? You spend about twenty years reading and writing and doing it over and over, feeling like you're in purgatory." But even as my anger flashed, I knew it was pointless. Why bother talking to someone capable of asking a question like that? I mumbled something and hung up. (Hanging up a phone was a much more satisfying gesture than today's tapping a screen.)

I'm still learning to write. For the past forty years I've been fooling around with fiction, trying to figure out how and why it works. Like so many others, I looked for guidance from books. I read a bunch of them and eventually I found two that spoke to me in a way that made sense. They might not be your cup of tea, but they suited some of the things I realized I needed to learn and they talked in a way that that seemed helpful. One is *Techniques of the Selling Writer* by Dwight V. Swain and the other is *On Film-Making* by Alexander Mackendrick.

Here's one of the things Dwight Swain says about "the people in your story," which is the title of Chapter 7 in *Techniques of the Selling Writer*, permission for this excerpt from the University of Oklahoma Press, copyright 1973.

The impossible, the unattainable, the forbidden, the disastrous: These constitute the raw materials with which you combine courage, in order to create story people who excite and fascinate.

Conversely, you cut deep into your chances for any broad success if you choose your major characters from the ranks of the weak and passive. Nothing is drearier than the story that centers on dull, apathetic people borne down by trivial problems..."

That's what I went for, the forbidden and about to be disastrous, characters who excite and fascinate (well at least get some interest). And the reader sees them that way not because of who they are, but *for what they're doing.* These are the people most fun for me to write about because—I guess I can't help it—I'm writing for the reader who likes that kind of stuff.

There is, of course, another side to all this. If you're a sensible person, head screwed on right, not interested in working at writing, if you're hanging out at a site like Burrst to rattle off some words when you feel like it and stick it up there for your friends and the heck of it, that's entirely fine with me. By all means go for it, have fun. As Dwight Swain says, everyone has a God-given right to go to hell in his own way—and don't let anyone kid you out of yours.

People seem to be endlessly curious about the creative process, some because they just can't understand at all how it happens, others because they'd like to learn to do it, or to do it better. I know I was numbered among that second group, until I finally figured out pretty much how to do it, sometimes, more or less, for better or for worse. (As Hub Miller pointed out to me once, "It's a fountain, not a machine.")

For me it often begins in the very early morning hours, in that little period between beginning to wake up and finally getting out of bed, when I've found it's a good time to think about things. I've been working on two stories, depending on how each feels at any given time, and one of them is *Death Leap,* which requires a scene in a public stadium. (That story is the last one in this collection.) My imagination used San Diego's Qualcomm Stadium for this setting, even though the stadium has been torn down.

So I was thinking about this scene and Qualcomm one morning. Then I started to think about how it once was named Jack

Murphy Stadium before Qualcomm bought the naming rights, or how, actually, the name was sold out from under old dead Jack Murphy just for some money. Jack Murphy had been a San Diego sportswriter whose tireless advocacy in favor of building this city arena earned him the posthumous honor of having it named for him. I wondered how Jack Murphy's heirs and friends felt about erasing Jack Murphy's name and putting up Qualcomm's name instead.

From there it was only a small step to thinking about how a living person might want to memorialize his name so that it would echo down through the halls of time, and I imagined this very rich Bill Gates-like person (but a lot less secure in his identity than the real Bill Gates) offering (for example) a thousand dollars to each family if they named a newborn child "Bill Gates" (or whatever his name is in the story, you get the idea).

How many folks would welcome a thousand dollars just for a little writing on a piece of paper (they would have to furnish a notarized birth certificate to collect the money).

All of a sudden, you've got fifty thousand kids born this year named Bill Gates. A lot of them are Hispanic, a lot of them are African Americans, a lot of them are Caucasian. They all have the same name.

A few years later, the first grade teacher at Emmanuel Kant Elementary School is looking at a class of thirty kids, and all fifteen of the boys are named Bill Gates, and moreover three girls are also named Bill Gates (see how that happened? A small surprise. Readers like surprises.) To keep the classroom organized, she gives each Bill Gates a number. But which kid gets to be Number 1? Some kid comes home and says, "I'm Number 2." The parents aren't going to like that.

The Social Security Administration is faced with issuing 50,000 new Social Security numbers to infants all named Bill Gates. The bureaucrats get plenty mad about all the problems and confusion. Hospital administrators across the country become deathly afraid of mixing up the babies in the nursery, all of them named Bill Gates.

Everyone, all across the country, with any responsibility for keeping track of who's who is really fed up with that megalomaniac, spreading his name across the country, making their jobs more difficult. But expectant parents love it. It's expensive to have a child, and the thousand dollars helps.

The whole thing becomes a big national story, some hate it, some love it. Then the marketing guy at Verizon Wireless (or some company like that) is watching the news one night, and he gets a bright idea. Three weeks later, after appropriate legal review, Verizon offers $1,500 to the parents who will name their newborn "Verizon."

Then the Catholic Church offers $2,000 to all parents who will name their newborn "Holy Redeemer."

This is capped by the Pentecostals, who offer $2,500 for "Saved by the Blood of Jesus."

Oh, no, this is too much. Lawsuits are filed. One of them wends its way through the system and finally reaches the Supreme Court. The issue is profound: Is anything and everything for sale under the Constitutional right of freedom of commerce and speech, regardless of its impact on society at large? The case will be argued by a young woman named Bill Gates, while the government's position will be represented by Solicitor General Holy Redeemer.

That's how it works for me. In each of these situations you can imagine the characters who would be involved in the conflict.

I think the key to imagination is mentally just standing aside and (after politely requesting your subconscious to come up with the solution to a problem), allowing it to happen. Yes, it's very Zen, isn't it?

How About Creativity?

When I first began to understand that I had the capacity to exercise my imagination in ways that others thought strange or not typical, I didn't think too much about it. It seemed to me that everyone I knew had the same innate capacity to be creative, many of them much more than me, while a good many people simply chose not to indulge in those peculiar exercises.

"The stiffs," as a college chum characterized them, they could be a *little* creative when they had to, but it wasn't a trait that they found particularly respectable or desirable. Not something to be pursued, certainly.

So what's the essential source of creativity? As the years went by, I began to realize, and I think now, that most people have a strong desire to get all the gestalts closed as rapidly as possible. That terminology comes from years ago, when guys like Fritz Perls and the ideas of Gestalt Psychology and the Human Potential Movement were in vogue. The most basic rule of gestalt is the law of *pragnanz*, which is German for proximity. (It's so much more impressive in German. When you put it in caps italic bold, doesn't **PRAGNANZ** look like a Mercedes Benz snarling?)

The idea of gestalt supposes that people generally want to experience things in as good a gestalt way as possible. In this sense, good means so that they can be most easily understood. It works like this:

• If something is missing, our mind adds it, closing the gestalt.

• Our mind groups similar things together, making the gestalt complete.

• Things that are close together are seen as belonging together, simplifying the gestalt.

• Symmetrical images are seen as belonging together regardless of distance, because that makes them more easily understood.

• Our mind continues a pattern even after it stops, or, as I like to think of it, the gestalt of the situation comedy is new episodes continue to be made long after all the ideas have passed away.

Under the gestalt theory, these tendencies not only apply to images, but to thought processes, memories, and our understanding of time.

What all this adds up to, if you go for the theory, is that people generally have a tendency to want to make up their minds, to have all decisions cut and dried, right away, no delay. In other words, they are seeking what in music is called resolution, that final chord at the end that tells you everything has been worked out and now the piece is complete.

This way of looking at things helps explain the great frustration with the now-ended war in Afghanistan, and any other situation where there isn't a ready-made silver bullet that will in one stroke (quickly, for God's sake) provide an answer and solve the situation.

This theory also goes a long way toward explaining talk radio. The talk radio hosts (all of them, of all persuasions) rely on arousing in the audience a feeling of outrage over whatever the cause of the day might be. That outrage of the day is then put into contrast with the silver bullet of the day, which is an instant and perfect solution, and there you have the popularity of talk radio. "Jesus," people think, "if only (insert name here) were in the White House."

But I'm getting far afield.

So, to put this all together, I think creative people are those who, for one reason or another, are more or less comfortable with open gestalts. When they see a pattern of dots, they don't automatically close it into a circle. They notice the background as well as the foreground, knowing that the foreground figure *depends* on the background against which it is seen. They look not just at the foreground figure, but the relationships involved. They know that printed black ink is transparent (hence the need for double black, which actually is a thing) and changes color with the color it is printed on. They don't have to have their mind made up about all contingencies in order to be comfortable in their habitual mindset. They notice the change of name, and they wonder what would happen if…

Another way to look at imagination and creativity is through the lens of the Big Five personality traits, or the Five Factor Model. People who are creative tend to score high in Openness.

So how does one become creative?

The good stuff springs up from your subliminal writing mind when you get your intellectual b.s. out of the way. This is why we often get ideas while in the shower, driving on the freeway, in that period between sleeping and waking. Get your "intellect" really bored so it goes to sleep, and what's left is the creative imaginative part of your mind.

I've been cultivating this for a long time (as I transition this manuscript into Vellum, I'm 86), and I can report that the more you do it, try to get out of the way so that the good stuff can bubble up, the more easily it seems to happen. You can't feel these changes, the same way you can't feel the blood flowing through your arteries, because you don't have any nerves in your arteries, and you don't have any nerves in your brain telling you how your brain feels, so you have to keep at it even though you don't get immediate reinforcement. But your writing gets better and (saints be praised) it gets easier.

You can find a fuller description in the book *Drawing on the Right Side of the Brain* by Betty Edwards. One of the exercises she suggests for improving drawing skills is take the object you're trying to draw and turn it upside down. When the object's meaning is removed, attention to the details is improved.

Jill Bolte Taylor, PhD, gives an extensive explanation about how the two sides of the brain operate in her book *Stroke of Insight*. She was a trained and published neuroanatomist when she had a stroke on the left side of her brain. She *knew* she was having a stroke, and recounts what it was like for the person having the stroke. That part of her brain that judges, that keeps the creative stuff at bay, that was disappearing, and what was left was the other part. It's quite an interesting read for someone curious about the creative process and how it works. In the book she also describes the steps anyone can take to have a healthier outlook on life by allowing the right side of the brain to be more active.

In brief, the right side of the brain is free to think intuitively, be spontaneous, carefree and imaginative. But it's the left side, the judgmental, accounting, down to business side that typically dominates. (This left-right is how it is for a majority of people, but for some the sides are reversed.)

Where Story Ideas Come From

Everyone's different, so I can only speak for myself. But, who knows, I might not be that different from you.

There's a pattern to the origins of stories in this book, and it's this: they have originated not because I was sitting around trying to think up a story; rather, they have come about when I was *trying to solve a problem.*

For example, with *Actor*, there was a technique I wanted to try, plus an image I'd written years before, and the problem was how to bring the two together into a story. Three of the stories in this book were written in response to contests, so the problem was posed for me. With the others, the idea came from an image that somehow captured my imagination—it gives me the feeling of dropping into focus, as if the right side of my brain grabs it and allows it to blossom (*"I've got that, now what story might it go in?"*). In one case, the story came out of a wealth of information that was unique and wildly different than anything I'd run across before, and that information turned into *Negative Twenty Questions* ("*Oh, this is so much good stuff, I've got to write a story with it.*"), which also happened to be in response to a contest.

The problem was, what story fits all this stuff I'm learning about?

Ideas come not from trying to think up an idea, but rather from trying to solve a problem.

In one case, which happened to me last week, since I finished this book (I'm adding this section just prior to publication), I felt like writing something and Scribophile was running a contest called "Flash Flood Warning" for flash fiction, limit 1,000 words.

I started noodling around on the keyboard and began with my favorite starting word, "When…", the trick I learned from reading Donald E. Westlake. The problem was flash flood, what's a flash flood story? Not rain, everyone will be writing about rain. How about unreal rain?

> When the sound guy, head cocked to one side, was satisfied, stopped moving his hand up for more rain, down for less rain, when he was finally pleased that the level of rain on the tin awning outside the tacky motel room was just right—not so much that it would drown out the dialogue, not too little so that it wouldn't read on the soundtrack—when he had the rain at just that certain level, he gave the thumb and finger okay sign and made his way out of the sagging motel room door, closing it carefully.

A sound guy and a tacky motel room with a sagging door, fake rain on a tin awning, obviously we're making a movie. It's a long sentence, but it's all about one thing, presents one image, so I thought it was okay. But what next? Since the story is going to need people and we're in a tacky motel room, let's have a woman and put her on a bed in some sort of pose.

> The woman lounging in her slip on the uneven mattress of the twin bed, one knee raised, arms stretched over her head so that her hands reached the worn wooden head-

board, who had been watching the sound guy calibrate the rain, spoke in somber tones, changing the line to fit what she might have felt at that moment if she'd been someone else. "I hate the rain. Sometimes I see myself dead in it."

When you don't know what else to do, quote a famous line about rain. Obviously in the next paragraph, I need to bring in another character, and also obviously, he would be her husband, and since she's an actor, he would be one too. The way they turned out, the two of them, they became much older, much less successful, versions of Elizabeth Taylor and Richard Burton, sort of the way they were in *Who's Afraid of Virginia Woolf*, but I never allowed this to become too explicit, or at least I don't think I did.

"Are you going to stick to the character in the script, or are you going to wander off and be Catherine in *A Farewell to Arms*?" Until now he was scarcely noticeable, the man in the cheap, wrinkled suit who stood near the old fashioned double-hung window, partially in shadow, though it wasn't certain where the shadow originated, the room being dimly lit in shades of blue with a diffuse pink tint from the motel's neon light that entered through the window. The man scratched a match and brought it up to light his *faux* cigarette. He was unshaven and had once been handsome, but now his jowls sagged, his eyes showed too much disappointment, too many years.

The rain chattered on the tin awning.

That's how my writing mind decided it would go. A movie set, everything ready, the actors waiting. I just kept going, and a few hours later, stiff and tired, I had the first draft, between 900 and 1,000 words. And I had a deep feeling of satisfaction, the feeling a writer always has when the first draft is finished.

So that's the best information I can provide on where story ideas come from: they emerge out of problems. Set yourself a problem and let your writing mind work it out.

If there is a secret, it's this: I love doing this stuff. It's just so much fun.

Intro to Death Leap

I finished this story about twelve years ago, then I seemingly lost it on my hard drive. (The last time I changed external hard drives and moved everything to the new one, there were about 90,000 files involved.)

Then, when I was putting things together for this book, I ran a search one day and found this story, more or less as it appears, complete in a PDF file, all finished and formatted.

I don't know what happened, whether distracting things were going on IRL, but I never sent it out, never tried to find a publisher for it. I think now I should have, I think it's reasonably entertaining. And I do like Harry, despite his shortcomings. (Shortcomings, is that what they are?) And I certainly admire Christine.

13

Death Leap

It's not so simple to let someone kill themselves on national TV, especially when there's a lot of money involved.

A HALLWAY WITH THICK FOREST-GREEN carpet led somewhere, tall doors along the hallway, all closed. Then Harry came to a set of double doors that were open wide, people inside a huge room.

The chatter and laughter beneath the sparkling chandeliers, the clink of ice in glasses, the room's richness, the women's dresses, the lush music, the happy beehive of contentment, he wanted to be part of it.

There was a placard on a stand at the entrance to the ball-room announcing a private party hosted by Klepner Reality Productions.

Reality.

Perhaps that was why he had come here.

When he saw the word like that, he realized he had been worried about reality.

Just inside the door was a bar, a bartender in a white jacket serving drinks. Harry asked for a dextroamphetamine sulfate spansule.

"Sorry," the bartender said, "this is the only import I got." He set a glass and a can of Heineken on the bar. Harry smiled, happy he was being treated as if he were one of them, as if he belonged here.

Turning from the bar with the icy wet can of Heineken in his hand, Harry saw the woman across the room and right away he knew she was the one. She was facing away from him, all he could see was her back, her beautiful long bare back, short dark blonde hair, a shimmering green dress. And her elbows, her elbows were lovely. She was certainly the one. All he had to do was make her want him. He asked the bartender who these people were, who was that woman in green.

The bartender didn't look up from rinsing glasses, Harry could see he didn't care about the beautiful woman, didn't care about anything.

"Some kind of TV deal," he muttered, "TV people from L.A."

TV! Well! Harry had watched plenty of TV. He knew he could make a TV woman want him. Maybe not right away. First he would have to serve her. He would be whatever she wanted him to be. Yes, what would a TV woman want him to be? Something special, something she'd never seen. And then she would want him and then they would love each other.

Harry walked across the room, slipping between the groups of people, a small man, hardly noticed. He stopped behind the beautiful woman in the green dress. He pressed the can of beer to her bare back and whispered, "I think I can fly."

The can was shockingly cold. Instantly furious, Christine barely heard what the guy said. She whirled around, her glass of

Cabernet slopping all over his shirt front, her elbow sending the can of beer tumbling and spinning, spewing foam across ballroom's laminate maple floor.

A pool of embarrassed silence spread around them.

Christine was ready to deck the creep.

He was a skinny little guy maybe five foot three, shaggy hair, wearing a filthy, wrinkled seersucker suit. He had a goofy half-smile on his face and big, begging brown eyes, innocent and helpless.

"What the fuck do you think you're doing?" She wasn't about to let any Vegas creep—or any L.A. creep, either, for that matter—get away with that kind of abuse of her personal space and dignity. Especially not when she was wearing a gorgeous jade green silk lamé backless gown that made her look pretty damn stunning. At six-five in heels, slender and elegant, she towered over him. The guy just stood there, looking up at her.

She was ready to deck him, but Jesus, he was like a cross between a homeless person and a dime store Chia Pet. Her nervous system was primed, demanding something. She tossed her wine glass after the beer can. It shattered on the floor. Christine didn't take her eyes off the guy. The breaking glass and frightened intake of breath from a couple of nearby women felt good. Yeah, you damn well better be afraid.

The shrimp wasn't out of the woods. Her fists were balled. A single wrong move, one wrong word, to hell with preliminaries, to hell with his hangdog look, she would put him on his ass, hopefully with a bloody nose.

"You little shithead," she said, making no attempt to keep her voice down. "What the fuck do you think you're doing?"

"I'm sorry," the guy stammered, babbling. "The bartender said you were on television and I wanted to tell you I can fly. You could put me on TV and I could fly for you."

Christine looked at his blushing face, felt her anger leaking away. Hell, she couldn't smack this sorry little fucker. And what had he said?

"You can what?" she said, "you can fly?"

The guy tried a smile and nodded.

Then Russell, one of the VPs, was at her side. "You got a problem with this guy, Christine?"

"He says he can fly."

"Great," Russell said. He gave the guy the once-over. "That's just great. Now maybe it's time you ran along, pal."

Good old Russell, the pudgy fifty-year old exec making like a tough guy. "Wait a sec, Russ." She turned back to Harry. "How would you fly?"

His face was confused for a moment, then cleared as he found an answer. "We could go up to the roof and I could jump off."

Looking at him, Christine felt it, if she encouraged him just a little, he would march right up to the roof and do it. She studied the weird little guy in the wrinkled suit. The stains on his shirt and jacket: was that the wine she had dumped on him or was that brown stuff dried blood? He didn't appear to be bleeding and he didn't look dangerous.

"If you jumped off the roof," she said carefully, "it's most likely you would kill yourself."

"Maybe," he said. "Maybe I'd prob'ly die. But maybe God would float me down to earth. And you would pay me, right?"

Christine and Russell turned to each other and burst out laughing. That morning at breakfast Arnold Klepner, frustrated by the absence of new, truly dynamic ideas, ideas he could pitch to the networks, had said what they needed was someone willing to jump off the Brooklyn Bridge, preferably during East Coast prime time.

"Whoever said life doesn't imitate art?" Russell said to Christine, then turned to Harry. "Sure we'd pay you, but if you were dead, the money would go to your estate, not to you."

The little guy perked up. "Did you ever think," he said, his voice soft, hesitant, "did you ever think that if you jumped off a place so high that you would die, that maybe if it wasn't your time to die, or maybe if you wanted to enough, you could really fly just that once? Like on a TV show? Maybe, if it wasn't your time, God would float you down. Did you ever think of that?"

Christine looked into his appealing brown eyes.

"No," she said, "I never thought of that."

"Well, maybe it's true," he said softly.

"And maybe it's not."

"We could find out. How much would you pay me?"

"How does a million dollars sound?" It just came right off the top, a producer's run-of-the-mill response, everybody's idea of big money but really, in today's economy, chump change.

The guy smiled. "Really? A million dollars? I'd be a millionaire?"

Russell put in, "You'd be a dead millionaire."

"Yes, but a millionaire. I'd be a millionaire."

"You'd be a millionaire very, very briefly," Christine said.

Christine watched him straighten to his full height. "Yes, but the important thing is that I would be one. I've always dreamed of being a millionaire."

Christine wondered whether he was nuts or some kind of druggie. Whatever it was, he had a warm, fuzzy quality. "You're a wacky little fruitcake, aren't you?"

The guy grinned and nodded. Christine had the impression he would be whatever she wanted him to be.

"I would be famous, wouldn't I?" he asked. "I mean, if I jumped?"

Russell's tone was sardonic. "If you jumped off the top of a seventeen-story hotel and killed yourself on network TV? Especially if you did it in Vegas, yeah, you'd be pretty famous for maybe a week, ten days. After that you'd be two lines in Wikipedia nobody ever looked at."

Listening to Russell, looking at the little guy, Christine saw the whole goddamned thing: the show, the concept, everything dropped into focus, just like that. She could see the effect it would have. It would be pervasive. It felt like a mystical vibration going off in her mind, harmonics rippling. It would resonate. Oh, yes, it would resonate and it would have traction. It would burrow into people's imaginations and it would drive them to the tube. They wouldn't have any choice, they would have to watch. A huge audience. Her feeling was so strong she involuntarily looked around, as if someone might overhear what was going through her mind. Was anyone looking at her? They were, but not with that understanding. No, of course not.

She turned back to the little guy. "If I produced the show you'd be famous," she said. "I can't vouch for it if anybody else produced it."

Russell laughed. "Jesus, Christine, you're too much. You want everything, don't you?"

She looked at him. Of course he would see it that way. Let him think what he wanted. "Hey," she said, "he likes me better than he likes you. Why can't you just accept it?"

"I would only do it for you." The little guy was staring at Christine with a look of devotion. Christine saw it and smiled in return. She'd seen that look before. He needed a woman on a pedestal, she knew how to play that.

"See what I told you?" Christine said sliding close to Russell and giving him a hip bump, as if she were moving him out of the play on a basketball court. "He's mine. I saw him first and he's mine."

"What's your name, little man?" Christine asked.

He told her.

"Well, Harry, you're kind of a mess. I think we should get you cleaned up, then get a couple drinks and sit down and have a nice talk. How does that sound?"

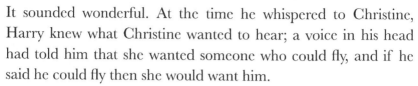

It sounded wonderful. At the time he whispered to Christine, Harry knew what Christine wanted to hear; a voice in his head had told him that she wanted someone who could fly, and if he said he could fly then she would want him.

He wasn't quite sure how he had arrived at the hotel or this room. When he couldn't stand being in the apartment anymore, so close to the bedroom, the room he knew he would never again be able to enter, he left the apartment, walking the streets until he found himself at this hotel. He knew his suit was wrinkled and he had LaDonna's blood all down his front. A security guard at the door was looking at him, and Harry could tell that he was thinking that Harry shouldn't be there. They had thrown him out of that other casino, when, last night? Harry took out a twenty dollar bill and held it in his hand. If they saw you had money in your hand they thought you were going to gamble and they left you alone. Harry had learned that.

A couple days before, La Donna had left, as she sometimes did, and sitting alone in the apartment, Harry came to the realization that the elbows are an essential part of civilization.

Without the use of their elbows, most men would not be able to make love—at least, not in the missionary position. Without elbows, the arms and hands would be much less useful. Yet did the elbows complain? No. Though neglected, they were always there, ready to serve.

Carefully, with his calligraphy pen, Harry wrote out a card:

> Long Sleeves Were Given to Man
> To Enable Him to Conceal his Elbows

He taped the card to the mirror in the bathroom.

When he went out to the supermarket, he put on a long-sleeved shirt, though the Las Vegas sidewalk shimmered in the heat. At the supermarket he stood in the express checkout line behind a girl in a short-sleeved blouse. She was young and her elbows were smooth and fresh. Virgin elbows.

He leaned forward and whispered in her ear, "Your elbows are showing." When she turned around, Harry smiled at her. She gave him a dirty look. He hadn't really meant anything except to let the girl know that he understood exactly what she was doing by letting anyone and everyone see her naked elbows.

As was his custom when LaDonna was away, Harry spent the next day giving the apartment a thorough cleaning. Harry loved LaDonna's apartment. He felt so lucky to have a place to live. Before she had brought him home with her, he had been living in a large cardboard box in a dark corner of an underground parking garage.

Harry had learned that nothing means anything when you don't know your place in the world. When you're not wanted, nothing matters. He had only been able to come to this realization after he began living with LaDonna in her beautiful apartment. He loved LaDonna and she loved him. They belonged together. Harry had a place with LaDonna, and everything mattered again.

After two hours with Harry, Christine began to think—yeah, there were a lot of problems—but she began to think that it might actually be possible.

For one thing, he was completely amenable to whatever she suggested. She made him empty his pockets. There were some odd pieces of paper, receipts from a supermarket and a liquor store, and a plastic container holding three pills. Dexedrine. The prescription label had someone else's name on it, she paid no attention. She dumped the pills in an ashtray, put the vial beside them and waved a waiter over to take it all away. Harry had forty dollars in his thin wallet and an old expired New York State driver's license, nothing else, no pictures, no business cards, no credit cards. He said he had no home and no place to stay, no luggage, no clothes. She took him down to the front desk and got him the cheapest room in the hotel and put it on the company credit card.

She was a little surprised the next morning when he obediently followed her instructions and showed up for breakfast. She had thought he would pick up and vanish, never to be seen again.

But there he was in the coffee shop, looking pathetic.

After breakfast, Christine took him out front and asked a cabbie to take them to the nearest Sears or Penney's. She explained the whole thing to Harry on the cab ride. At the store, as she bought him two sets of clothes, one to wear and the other in a shopping bag, she explained the whole thing again. She made him leave his old clothes on the fitting room floor.

By the time they got back to the hotel, she thought that if she didn't have Harry primed and ready to go by now, she never would. She called Klepner's room, and he said to come up in an hour. She dragged Harry into the hotel barbershop, got him a haircut and a shave, and by the time he was finished, Harry looked like a small, sensitive Montgomery Clift, except not so handsome and a lot more lost.

Harry handled the interview with Klepner just the way she had told him to. When Klepner asked, Harry told him that if it wasn't his time yet, he might actually be able to fly, and how he had always wanted to be a millionaire. When Klepner got to the difficult questions, such as did Harry understand that he would probably be killed in his attempt to fly, Harry was ready with the answer: "Oh, yes," he said. "I understand that I'll prob'ly die. But that's all right. I'll die a millionaire, and that's what I've always wanted, to be a millionaire when I die."

Klepner actually tried a couple of times to get Harry to change his tune, admit some doubts, and Christine was surprised at Klepner's unexpected show of—what was it, integrity? human concern?—but Klepner didn't try too hard, and Harry was shy and wholesome and stuck to his story.

"Well, geezus," Klepner said, "You just might have a show here, Christine. But there's a lot of loose ends. We need a venue, for one thing, that could be a problem. I'll pitch it to the networks and let's see what happens."

And then, as soon as Klepner started to think about his network pitch, Christine could see it on his face, "We could call it, Will He Fly with a bunch of question marks after it. Yes, that would really work, Will He Fly???"

"Isn't that a little close to that Letterman schtick?" Christine asked. "That stupid thing he used to do, Will It Float?"

"No, no, it's a great title. It's got mystery, a touch of the occult. The occult is big right now. Will He Fly question mark, question mark, question mark, I like it."

Christine kept her mouth shut. Successful is no insurance against dumb; it was not the first time the thought had occurred to her.

When LaDonna went away, she left money for Harry. This time Harry found two one-hundred dollar bills under her hair brush on the dressing table. Harry put the money in his wallet and set out for Fremont Street, downtown Las Vegas.

Harry knew he was safe in LaDonna's apartment, but when he went out into the city weird things always happened to him. He felt as though he were in a zone of destructive radiation, an area where the unholy alliance of the Mafia and the Nuclear Testing Center created a vector for all the evil in the world. Harry understood exactly why the U.S. Government conducted its underground nuclear tests beneath the desert near Las Vegas. They were chasing the Beast. Harry knew about the huge, dark

Beast that dwelled in tunnels beneath the Las Vegas desert. Harry had realized this the first time he had flown into Las Vegas. As the plane descended, Harry had looked out the window at the sharp, scabby cinnamon hills, the raised desert ridges, and he had seen with his own eyes that the ridges were the bony spines of the Beast that lurked at the edges of that corrupt city. Despite this, or perhaps because of it, Harry felt drawn to this place.

The staff flew back to L.A. that afternoon, Christine booking a ticket for Harry. She got him a room in a hotel not far from her apartment in West Hollywood, and got on the phone with Securitas, and inside ninety minutes she had a guy with Harry twenty-four seven. It was expensive as hell, but, she thought, necessary.

She had dinner that night at a neighborhood Italian place with Harry and the Securitas guy on the night shift, a big handsome Black man named Hamilton. She and Hamilton just sat there and looked at each other across the table as Harry rambled on about the importance of elbows and the beast that lived under the desert. The next day she had Harry moved from the tenth floor hotel room with balcony to a ground floor garden suite that had a very high fence around a tiny patio. She hired a car service for them and gave the Securitas guy on shift that day her company credit card and told him to get Harry some clothes, including a suit and tie and shoes, and to take him anywhere he wanted to go, the movies, Disneyland, the Magic Castle, wherever.

Klepner was pitching the show left and right and the first day he stopped in the doorway of Christine's office and said that pay-per-view was no problem, if nothing else was possible, they could always do pay-per-view, but HBO was a possibility. When they found out that HBO might want the show, Fox made a high-dollar bid, contingent on the whole thing passing the sniff test, which was cool network attorney talk for due diligence, including a location for the event, a meeting with Harry, and the okay from a medical expert.

It made sense to have the show originate in Las Vegas. Unusual entertainment, Las Vegas, the two were made for each together. And after all, Las Vegas seemed to be as close to a hometown for Harry as anything else.

She made an appointment with one of the senior guys at the Visitors and Convention Bureau and took a morning flight. The executive, dressed like a banker, listened politely to her explanation.

"He's going to kill himself?" he said, when she was finished. "You want to do it in Vegas?"

"That's the show."

"Well, for us, that's maybe not such a good idea. Understand, we've got people coming in here from all over. Some of them end up gambling away everything they have, I mean, they lose every single thing they have in the world. It's too bad, but that's kind of the way this business works sometimes. Then they decide there's only one way out. No thanks. We've got enough people killing themselves in Vegas already, we don't need one more on national TV."

Christine had better luck in San Diego, where she presented to the management of Qualcomm Stadium. They were ready to listen. The Padres had left for a new downtown ballpark, and the NFL team, the Chargers, were taking off for the richer pastures of Chula Vista or Los Angeles or Las Vegas or San Antonio or someplace. Stadium management was desperate to keep their jobs and delay the time when the stadium would be leveled for condos and shopping centers. So the deal was made for the Fourth of July, Qualcomm Stadium. Determined to control everything, Christine asked about tickets and pricing. They took her to an office where she looked over the shoulder of the woman who was the ticket expert at the onscreen seating system. An algorithm cascaded ticket prices from the cheapest seats to the most expensive skyboxes, setting the relative price for every seating category in the sixty-five-thousand-seat stadium.

"Higher," Christine said, "Jack it up, jack it up." When the average ticket cost reached a thousand dollars, Christine said, "Let's try that."

"We've never priced anything so high," the woman turned her frightened face to Christine.

"We can always come down if we need to," Christine said. "It's harder to go up." She patted the woman on the shoulder, and spoke the line that all producers soon learn, the line that makes people do what you want them to do: "Don't worry about it, I take full responsibility."

Will He Fly??? was set to go.

Media-wise, the weeks prior to the announcement of Will He Fly??? had been a slow boat to nowhere. Everyone in the country was dispirited over the various wars that seemed endless. They wanted to hear no more, they yearned for some kind of distraction. Yet there had been no cheerleaders mysteriously missing in the Caribbean; no look-alike high school shoot-'em-up plots uncovered—not for a couple weeks—no brides molested or grooms tossed overboard on cruise ships, nothing.

As a result, the media landed on Will He Fly??? with both feet.

But they didn't call it Will He Fly??? As it turned out, it didn't matter what Klepner or the network wanted to name the show, the press dubbed it Death Leap. It was above the fold on the front page of many of the major dailies; there was a terrific photo of Harry, looking very Montgomery Clift, on the front page of what might have been every tabloid in the English-speaking world, and many in Europe and Asia, as well, and there was only one topic on talk radio and tabloid TV. Death Leap: Was it ethical? Was it right or wrong? Was it good or bad? Did everyone have a right to do whatever they wanted, or would these forces destroying our culture stop at nothing in pursuit of the Almighty Dollar?

Once the tabloid TV shows, the newspapers, the magazines and talk radio focused on the show, all of them calling it Death Leap, it took the network three days to decide to formally change the name of the show to Death Leap. Klepner agreed.

"Go along to get along," he said.

When they told Harry about the venue, he remembered the time in San Diego when he had waded out of the ocean and the policeman had been waiting for him. Harry had told the policeman how sorry he was that he had murdered the two women. He had meant, or he thought he meant, his mother and the Virgin Mary. He had left his mother alone to die in Albany, and because he had fallen away from the Mother Church, he was responsible for the death of the Virgin Mary. It had taken a long time, but finally a public defender pointed out the prosecution did not have sufficient evidence in the sexual molestation and murder of the spinster sisters in North Park, and they had let him go. During his last day in court, Harry had suddenly remembered why he had decided to go into the ocean in the first place, and thought his lawyer might want to bring it to the judge's attention. He had leaned across and whispered to him, "I'm a fish! I'm a fish!" The lawyer had told Harry to wait until the judge called a recess. But there was no recess. The charges were dropped and Harry was free.

Less than a week after the first press announcement, Christine took a call from the excited manager of Qualcomm Stadium.

The phones had been ringing off the hook, the website was on fire, the event was sold out; all the tickets were gone, they were grossing just under sixty-four million dollars.

Christine congratulated the guy, told him to pass along her thanks to the staff for a swell job, hung up the phone and stared at the computer screen in front of her. She clicked on the budget she had put together for the show, and entered the gross ticket sales. The spreadsheet deducted the ten percent for the stadium and then deducted the rows of various expense items. When Christine scrolled down she saw that some forty-three million dollars would drop directly to the production company's bottom line.

She looked at the screen, that bottom-line number, thinking about Harry, the show, her job and coming back to that number. Then she picked up the phone and dialed Teddy Solomon's office. An hour later, when he called her back, she insisted he meet her for a drink that night.

Christine went to Il Cielo straight from the salon. She caught her reflection with satisfaction as she walked in: tall and slender and beautiful, a California girl with taffy hair. She saw him stand up, smile, and wave when she entered, and she gave thanks, as she always did, that he was two inches taller than she.

They had met their freshman year. She was tall, he was taller, and they had become pals. Teddy invited her to a couple of pick-up basketball games; Christine had been all-state in high school and he thought it was hilarious when she dunked over the head of the poli-sci major who thought he was hot stuff on the court.

After graduation Christine had gone into media, then migrated to Southern California and television, while Teddy had left for law school, and was now at his second firm, this one in a Century City high rise. They emailed stupid jokes from time to time, and once in a while met for lunch. But tonight's meeting was something different.

"Here's what I've got," Christine said to him after the preliminaries. She told him about the developments of Death Leap.

"That's you? My God, Christine, I didn't realize that was your show!"

"It's mine and I'm up to my ears in it, and I need help. I want you to come to work for me."

"It would be great fun, but there's no way I can do it," Teddy said. "Two more years, I'm making partner. I'm on-track. That's what I've been working for."

"I only need you for five weeks. Five and a half weeks, max. The show airs, then it's over. It is, as you can understand, a one-shot." They laughed.

"I can't. You should see my desk, my office. I've got about sixteen stacks of documents all over the floor, a dozen client phone calls a day, five associates and a bunch of paralegals running their asses off, I've got a legal operation that's generating a ton of money for the firm."

Christine smiled to herself. This was what she loved, what she knew she was good at, rationalizing the world into a pattern that met her needs.

"What are you making, two-fifty, three?"

"Right in there, yeah," Teddy conceded.

"And when you make partner you'll be making a mil, a mil-five?"

"Probably."

"Okay, five weeks, I'll pay you two hundred thousand."

"Whether or not he jumps?"

"Oh, he's jumping, all right. I know he's going to jump," Christine said, though in her mind she wasn't nearly so sure, "and when the show airs, if he jumps, there's a hundred-k more in it for you."

"I'd love to, Christine, it would really be fun to work with you, and God knows I need a change, but I've got stacks of work, I've got the partners depending on me. The clients…"

Christine smiled. Objections were made to be overcome. "What would they do at the firm if you dropped dead, if some drunk driver smacked you with a Bentley while you were walking across Wilshire Boulevard? They'd figure it out, wouldn't they?"

"I suppose…"

"Of course they would. You've got five associates who probably know a lot more than you think they do."

"But I'm on-track for the partnership…"

"Teddy, five weeks from now you'll go back to the law firm as the hottest entertainment lawyer on the West Coast. You know you will. The lawyer for Death Leap. I'll get you billing as associate producer. You'll have a dozen new clients wanting you to come to dinner just to get the inside scoop, to show you off to their friends."

"You're probably right. I suppose I could ask the partners…"

"No," Christine said, "you don't *ask* the partners, you *tell* them. Tell them you're taking five weeks leave, that when you come back you'll be bringing all kinds of new business with you. Far from complaining, they'll be popping champagne corks."

Teddy looked at her across the table with what Christine hoped was something more than friendship. "You're really good at this aren't you?"

Christine nodded happily.

"I'll talk to them in the morning," Teddy said.

"No. Don't talk to them, no asking opinions, no *consulting* the partners like a flunky *consulting* the plantation owners." She made *consulting* sound like a character weakness. "Just tell them what you're doing. They'll respect you for it."

"Okay," she shifted gears, and Teddy grinned, seeing the change come over her, "now that you're on-board, here's what I need, and I need it for a meeting tomorrow."

It was dark by the time Harry stepped off the bus on Fremont Street, downtown. He started slow and easy, playing a little black-jack here, feeding the slots there, rolling the dice, opening himself up, letting everything come into his mind. Harry knew if he could only get his mind open and accepting enough, he could tune in to the hidden rhythms behind the dice and the cards and he would win.

Whenever he felt himself coming down, he took two of LaDonna's dexedrine spansule capsules. He had taken the plastic vial from the medicine cabinet. Harry liked the dexies. If there had been clocks in the casinos, he would have timed his doses, but since there were no clocks, he went strictly by his own sense of what his body and mind required in order to stay in motion.

Sometime after midnight the crowds thinned out and Harry found himself at a five-dollar blackjack table in a downtown casino. The only other gamblers at the table were Walt and Helen, a retired couple from Boulder City. They both kept their elbows covered and tried to joke with the dealer, whose name tag said Rosy. Harry asked Walt and Helen a few questions, trying to find out if they understood about the importance of wearing long sleeves. Rosy was hostile and intent on winning, as if her job depended on it, and after a while even Walt sensed it. He suggested they go out to the Strip and try the tables at Caesar's. He included Harry in the offer.

Sitting alone in the dark in the backseat of Walt and Helen's Cadillac, the cleanest car Harry had ever been in, he watched the lights of Las Vegas float past and he opened his mind. He sensed that Walt and Helen had been sent to lure him out to the Strip. Perhaps they were working him out toward the edge of town where the Beast could reach him with its claws. He found an umbrella that had worked its way down into the crack of the upholstery, the kind of umbrella that telescoped together, with a beige fabric sleeve and name tag on a bead chain. Perhaps the ribs of the umbrella would be protection against the claws of the

Beast. Harry put the umbrella under his shirt, the handle up in his armpit. He lost Walt and Helen in the casino and took a cab back downtown. His skin itched where the umbrella rubbed against him.

～

The next afternoon Christine walked into Klepner's office holding the contract that Teddy had drawn up.

"Yes, Christine?" Klepner looked up from his desk.

"I've got some good news, and some bad news," Christine said. "The good news is that the stadium sold out, and we're going to net around forty-three mil on ticket sales alone."

"My God, that's great!" Klepner said, coming around the desk to embrace her. Christine stepped back, keeping him at arm's length, forcing him to settle for a high five.

"But the bad news," Christine said, "is that I want executive producer billing on the show, and I want fifteen million as my cut of the ticket sales." She handed Klepner the contract.

He did what he could to talk her out of it, but Christine kept coming back to the same point: "I say jump, he jumps. I say don't jump, he doesn't jump and you've got no show. Then you've got the expense of giving back the ticket money and the embarrassment, not to mention the liability, of bailing out on the network, the advertisers, everybody."

Klepner bargained her down to ten million, they marked up the contract, both of them initialing the changes, and signed, and Christine walked out of Klepner's office with a smile on her face. The numbers had been Teddy's idea: Ask for fifteen, be willing to settle for five, and hope for the best. The fact she got ten assured Teddy of a one million dollar bonus. They had champagne cocktails, just one round, at Il Cielo that night after work before Christine had to leave for dinner with Harry and his keeper.

In the days and weeks that followed, a series of announcements were made about Death Leap, each adding a new level of excitement and controversy. A famous play-by-play announcer was signed for the show, along with two color commentators, one from the world of baseball, the other a semi-retired golf pro with an internationally known name. When reached at his country club, the golfer said, "I guess they picked me because I know a lot about trajectories and soft landings, but I don't know what those other guys are going to talk about."

Christine had another desk moved into her office and placed face-to-face with hers. "Partner desks," Teddy called them, and he started handling the myriad contractual agreements and various insurance coverages involved in the show.

They were together in the office long hours, and soon the closeness of school days returned, and then some.

Christine found herself coming around the desk at every opportunity to lean over Teddy's shoulder, put a hand on his arm, breath in his smell. And Teddy seemed to welcome these officemate gestures, and sometimes reached out to touch her hand, her arm, her shoulder. There were times when Christine just wanted to look up from her desk and say, "Listen, why don't we spend the afternoon at my apartment?" But always there was the show, the phone ringing off the hook, the calls from the media, each morning one crisis, then in the afternoon another.

For example, there were the rumors. The first was that Harry was a homosexual and an AIDS victim and had only months to live, regardless of whether or not he jumped. Christine arranged a full physical examination for Harry at the prestigious Scripps Clinic. The announcement that Harry was in excellent health was made by a Nobel laureate of unquestionable integrity. Of course, his association with this particular patient immediately brought his integrity into question. No direct reference was made to Harry's sexual preferences, although the doctor did state that Harry was "...a healthy young man and absolutely normal in every sense of the word."

Then there was the technical side. Articles were written about the structure of the five-hundred-foot tower and how its height would be accurately measured (a laser), the size and thickness of the concrete landing pad, and the effect that wind might have both on the tower and on the path that Harry would take when, and if, he jumped. Always of interest in such stories was the discussion of the speed that could be reached by falling objects.

The media put considerable pressure on the medical community to speculate on the probable outcome of Death Leap. Emergency room doctors and orthopedists were the specialties most in demand to comment on whether or not Harry might survive in the event he landed feet-first, head-first, on his stomach or his back, or what might be expected if he missed the concrete slab altogether and hit the turf in short center field. The physicians all said that the chance of survival was nil, but still the talk of this possibility seemed endless.

Following an article in a national grocery store tabloid, "How the Death Leaper Plans to Live!", it was announced that a blue ribbon committee would thoroughly inspect the concrete landing pad and the surrounding areas and verify the height of the tower minutes before the leap took place.

But would the television viewers actually be allowed to see what promised to be the gruesome spectacle of Harry smashed to death on the concrete landing pad?

The network executives became nervous about this, and Christine hired three engineers with experience in the automotive airbag industry, who designed a framework of aluminum poles and fabric that would deploy a concealing curtain on all sides of the landing pad. This curtain would be triggered by a falling object as it crossed an electronic beam just twenty feet above the concrete.

The object of most intense curiosity was, of course, Harry himself, who throughout the crescendo of publicity remained incommunicado at an undisclosed location. One tabloid reported he was somewhere in the Washington, D.C. area in a bombproof bunker. The comedians loved it: "If he's going to kill himself next week anyway, why does he need to be in a bombproof bunker?"

Armando Garcia, the newest and youngest detective at the crime scene, felt deeply insulted when assignments were handed out. The others got jobs that had some bearing on the investigation, but the Lieutenant stood there at the foot of the bed where the dead woman was stretched out, and when he came to Armando, he said, "You stick here, Garcia. Watch the forensics process the crime scene. Don't ask any questions, don't bother the scientists. Just watch and try to learn something."

Stick here, with that smell of the decaying corpse sinking into his clothes, into his hair and skin, watch a bunch of dorks with magnifiers and tweezers pick up hairs from the carpet? Wasn't he already trained? Didn't he already know the six basic crime scene search patterns?

He did what the Lieutenant said as long as he could stand it, watching the experts apply the spiral method in the bedroom, the zone pattern in the living room. He watched the Medical Examiner get clearance, then Armando went outside to the wrought iron railing and waited until they came out with the body in a body bag on a stretcher. He watched from above as they loaded it into a van and left for the morgue.

To hell with it, that was enough! Was Armando a full-fledged detective with a gold shield, or was he the squad's busboy, the servile Hispanic of the squad? What would come next? Would they have him making coffee runs and emptying the waste baskets? To hell with them!

When Armando Garcia got to the Medical Examiner's office forty minutes later, he found just what he expected: the autopsy had not yet started.

He stormed into the white, frigid examining room, its row of stainless steel tables, the sinks, the implements. One autopsy was underway while two young men in green lab coats chatted nearby.

"You!" Garcia stabbed his finger at one of the men. "You an ME?"

He was a Hispanic guy, slight, with short hair and gold-rim glasses. "Uh, yeah, assistant ME." He was uncertain.

"Armando Garcia, Homicide," Garcia had his badge out, his voice hard and loud, almost a yell. "The woman that just came in, LaDonna, why isn't she the fuck up on a table?"

The other green-coated man was taller, seemed unflustered. "That's scheduled for three o'clock."

"Three o'clock," Garcia said. "We got a killer on the fucking loose and you two are standing around beating your meat! I want that autopsy started now! Not in an hour, not at three o'fucking clock, but now!"

"Can't do it," the cool ME said. "It's on the schedule."

Garcia took two quick steps and put his face within inches of the ME's. "Fuck the schedule and fuck you, you candyass prick. You'll get her out here and start it now!"

"Jesus! Relax. Don't have a hissie-fit." He turned to the Hispanic. "Santiago, go get her."

"I'll fucking hissie-fit you, you faggot mother fucker," Garcia said.

Armando stood right there, at the cool ME's elbow, watching everything.

When the ME extracted the umbrella, bagged it and handed it to him, Garcia saw the little tag on the chain with the name and address all neatly printed, and felt a surge of excitement. These sex killers got so hot to trot they made profoundly dumb mistakes. This wasn't something he'd learned in class or read about or been told. This was something that came into his mind when he saw the name tag. It was undeniably true. There was the evidence, right in front of him.

He signed a possession receipt and took the evidence with him.

From his car he radioed Dispatch with an order to bring in this material witness and possible suspect, Walter Nicwandowski. He pulled over and read the name through the plastic, had to spell it three times over the radio. The subject would be found at the Boulder City address right there on the tag. No, it couldn't wait. Do it the fuck now. Another bunch of lazy sons-a-bitches who didn't want to do their job. Bring in the fucking suspect, *post haste.*

He had everything organized and laid out in one of the interview rooms when two officers brought Walter Nicwandowski in, his hands cuffed behind him, a uniform on each side.

He was an old guy, which didn't surprise Armando at all. Old and perverted, with a big belly, but broad-shouldered and muscular, like an iron-worker or shipfitter.

"Stand him right there," Armando motioned at the opposite side of the table. He wanted the suspect standing, looking at the crime scene photographs. They were still damp, fresh from the lab.

"I'm Detective Garcia, Walter, and I want you to take a nice close look at the results of your handiwork."

They were eight by tens, in color, wide shots, medium shots, close ups of LaDonna, legs spread, wrists tied to the headboard. It was all too clear how she had bled out onto the silk sheets of her king-size bed.

"Take a look at this one, Walter," Armando said, pointing to a close-up that showed some kind of bloody stump—the handle of the umbrella—protruding from LaDonna's body. "I bet you're plenty proud of that little piece of handiwork, aren't you, Walter?"

Walter Nicwandowski stared at the photo with a stricken

look. His face was grey with a stubble of beard. He made a guttural noise deep in his throat. Armando was feeling his stuff. He had this motherfucker right where he wanted him.

"But you made one little mistake, Walter," Armando said, triumph edging his voice. "One little fucking mistake."

From the seat of a chair beside him, Armando, with a flourish, produced the evidence bag holding the blood-streaked, disgusting mess recognizable as the umbrella. Garcia pressed down on the bag to show the name tag. "Well, well, well. Take a look at that. Walter Nick-fuck-up, Boulder City. Hey, that's you, isn't it, Walter? Oops, did you forget something inside this woman, Walter? Like your name and address?"

Nicwandowski's face went pale and distorted and his shoulders hunched against the cuffs behind his back. "Aww, arr," he gargled in his throat. Beads of sweat popped out on his forehead.

"I take that as a confession, Walter," Armando said, smug in the knowledge he had this son-of-a-bitch right where he wanted him. Detective Garcia was not without a poetic turn of mind. "You give a lethal injection, you get a lethal injection. Except yours is going to be on death row at Ely. You're going to get death, Walter," Armando said. "You might as well tell us everything, because you're as good as on death row right now, with the needle going into your arm. Think what it'll feel like when that great big fucking needle goes into your arm."

Nicwandowski collapsed, and would have hit the floor if it hadn't been for the officers on either side of him, who caught his upper arms. He was deadweight, his head falling limply. They lowered him to the floor.

"I've seen this little act before, Walter," Armando said, coming around the table. "You fake the faint while you think up an alibi. It ain't gonna work, baby!"

One of the officers kneeled by the stricken man. "I don't think he's breathing, Detective."

"Oh, for chrissake!" Armando got down beside

Nicwandowski, and when he realized that, indeed, there was no pulse in the carotid artery, he felt a sinking in the pit of his stomach, and he started CPR on the guy, while one of the patrolmen ran for the paramedics.

But it was too late. Walter Nicwandowski was declared dead at 2:37 that afternoon in Interview Room 1.

～

"Are you a dermatologist?" Harry asked the cocktail waitress at the Golden Nugget.

"Got a sunburn? I can get you some Solarcaine," the woman smiled at him.

"I have an umbrella under my arm and it's giving me severe dermatitis."

"Would you like a drink?"

"A screwdriver."

Harry had looked up dextroamphetamine sulfate in LaDonna's Physicians' Desk Reference. The manifestations of chronic amphetamine intoxication were severe dermatoses, marked insomnia, irritability, hyperactivity and personality changes. Maybe the vitamin C in the orange juice would help the itch.

When the cocktail waitress returned, Harry dropped a dollar chip on her tray.

"Do you think skin problems can cause a personality change?" he asked her.

"I'm really careful to stay out of the sun." She was blond, Harry could see she had once been young and innocent. Harry found himself wanting to serve her the way he served LaDonna. He wasn't sure if he was hearing music from somewhere or whether it was just in his head, but he knew he had to serve somebody.

"I could make you feel real good," he said to her. "I could serve you."

"I bet." She moved to another table.

Harry took two more dexedrine spansules with the screw-driver. Then he walked through the casino, looking at the women. He wondered if any of them would like it if he served them. There was one tall, strong-looking dark-haired woman, like LaDonna, that he was tempted to speak to, but he wasn't sure. He couldn't pick up any signals from her. He found a comfortable chair with an arm like a child's school desk and a little well containing keno forms and a black crayon. On a keno blank he carefully printed in all capitals PUSSY SERVED. Harry asked several of the cocktail waitresses and keno girls before finding one who gave him a safety pin. In the men's room, he pinned the sign to the lapel of his jacket. He admired the effect in the mirror. He wished he had brought his calligraphy pen and a nice white card.

"You're having a personality change now," he said to his reflection. He considered the sign. It seemed unfinished. He would have liked to have added INQUIRE WITHIN, or better yet, INQUIRE DEEP WITHIN. If he had brought his callig-raphy pen, he would have made a very good sign, but he didn't have his pen and this sign would have to do.

As Harry stepped out of the men's room, two burly security guards in khaki uniforms grabbed him by the arms, ripped off his sign, and shuttled him out a rear door to the alley behind the casino. Harry was frightened, his mouth dry, and he tried to explain to them that he wasn't serious, that he loved LaDonna and that he would never really serve anyone's pussy but hers. He was crying, but they didn't care. One of them held him by the shoulder and put his face close in front of Harry's. His breath smelled of beer and cigarettes. "Don't come back here. Do you hear me?"

Everything was ready, all preparations were made, the immense machinery of a live network show had all been set in motion, and Christine and Teddy sat in their L.A. office with their feet up on their desks and looked at each other.

Somehow, until now, it had all seemed like a board game, move this piece here, that one there. Now it was the day before Death Leap, and it had become real.

Teddy said, "You know, he's a crazy little son-of-a-bitch."

"Yeah," Christine replied, "but he's my crazy little son-of-a-bitch and no one else's."

"And you're going to make a lot of money off him."

"We both are. A lot."

"And he's going to kill himself."

"He's going to do it." It put a lump in Christine's throat when she said it.

"You sure?"

"Yeah. Actually, either he does it on the show or he'll do it later, by himself."

"How do you know?"

"I talk to him every night at dinner. He wants to die. He killed his mother and the Virgin Mary, two old ladies in San Diego and someone named LaDonna. He wants to die."

"Is that right? He killed a bunch of people?"

"I'm pretty sure he didn't kill the Virgin Mary, but the others, who knows? The way he talks, I think he might have."

"What did the shrink say?"

"The first shrink or the second shrink?"

"The first shrink."

"Once I told him the deal, the first shrink wouldn't even see Harry. He said that anyone who volunteered for our little entertainment was certifiable on the face of it, and he wouldn't have anything to do with it. So we ignored that guy and got ourselves another guy."

"And he said?

"He gave Harry all the tests, took two days, interviewed him, a complete physical and what he called an in-depth psychiatric profile and assessment."

"And?"

"Harry understands the consequences of his actions, he knows right from wrong, he's not clinically depressed, he doesn't... let me see..." Christine grabbed a three-ring binder on her desk and flipped it open, riffling through the pages and read from the report: "He doesn't fit into any of the categories in the Diagnostic and Statistical Manual of Mental Disorders of the American Psychiatric Association. His memory function is somewhat inconsistent, but his ability to reason logically is coherent and practical. Since the subject shows no signs of psychosis or deep neurosis, his mental health is therefore judged to be normal."

"He's normal," Teddy said.

"Yeah. As normal as you and I."

"You and me," Teddy corrected.

"Yeah, you and me."

"Maybe as normal as you," Teddy said, "but he's sure as hell not as normal as me. Who's this person he says he killed? Lah-who?"

"LaDonna."

"Let's see what we can find," Teddy said, turning to his computer, bringing up Google. He scrolled through the resulting list and clicked on an item. "She was killed in Las Vegas. When did you meet Harry?"

Christine checked her calendar and read the date.

"Her body was discovered three days after that, but they got the guy who did it," Teddy said, looking at a news item.

"Are you sure?" Christine came around to look over his shoulder, resting her hand on his shoulder. She resisted the impulse to spread her fingers, run her hand up through his hair, turn his head and kiss him.

"There it is. Picture of the cop who got the confession." Teddy scanned the news item, summing it up as he went. "A death-bed confession, it says, the guy, a retired guy from Boulder City, and look at that, incontrovertible key evidence, it says. Evidently the murder weapon was an umbrella that had this guy's ID on it. He was definitely the guy who killed her, and they got him. It wasn't Harry."

Christine's shoulders slumped. "I've got to talk to him."

"You said you talk to him every night."

"Yeah, but I've got to have a serious conversation with him. I can't let him do this."

"I'm coming with you."

"No, you can't. I have the Securitas guy there, so I'm perfectly safe, but Harry has this fixation on me. I can't bring another guy with me." She looked at him. "As much as I'd like to."

The Lieutenant convened the meeting in his office with Detective Armondo Garcia in the hotseat, a wooden straight-back chair directly in front of the Lieutenant's desk. Two detectives, Latimer and Stapleton, occupied the sofa.

Walking in the door to the meeting, knowing the situation, Latimer had whispered to Stapleton, "Ten bucks he turns the lemon into lemonade."

Stapleton already owed Latimer forty dollars in lemon-lemonade bets, but this time Stapleton had interviewed Walter Nicwandowski's wife, Helen, and he believed he had inside information.

"Fuck you," he whispered back to Latimer, "double or nothing."

The Deputy Chief of Police eased himself into a casual chair on the side of the office over in front of the windows, and

Sergeant Larkin, young, clean cut, articulate, a college grad, the departmental spokesman, sat in another. Behind Garcia in the straight back chair, a little to one side, at parade rest, stood the two patrolmen who'd been present in the interview room.

Once everyone had settled and he had their complete attention, the Lieutenant surveyed the silent room.

"What a fucking mess," he said, picking up the folded newspaper in front of him. Everyone knew the Lieutenant was staring at the big black headline they had all read earlier that morning: "Innocent Man Dies In Police Custody."

The Lieutenant looked up and spoke slowly to Detective Garcia, every word weighted with fury: "You fucked this up royally, you dumb fucking son-of-a bitch."

Garcia stared at the floor.

The Lieutenant picked up a pink telephone message slip from his desk and cleared his throat. "Let's open with this. The Chief Medical Examiner requests in the strongest possible terms that Detective Armando Garcia not be allowed within a hundred yards of the Morgue or the ME's office until further notice."

The Lieutenant gazed around the silent room. "This is so ordered. Do you understand this order, Detective Garcia?"

"Yessir," Garcia said softly.

"Okay," the Lieutenant said, "that's handled." He crumpled up the message slip and with a practiced gesture flipped it into the wastepaper basket beside his desk. He picked up a sheet of paper. "Now, as I understand the situation, this witness, Walter whatever-his-name-is, died of cardiac arrest in one of our interview rooms while being questioned by Detective Garcia, the newest and least experienced member of the Detective Squad." The Lieutenant stared at Garcia for a moment before continuing, his voice dropping to a quiet intensity. "You tell nobody nothing. You don't clear anything with your superior officer. You pull this old fucker in, accuse him of a sex crime, show him these ugly fucking pictures and this bloody fucking umbrella and then you're surprised when the son-of-a-bitch seizes up and dies on you. Is this an approximate summary of the situation, Detective?"

"Yessir."

"Anything to say in your own defense?"

Garcia lifted his head. "He confessed, Lieutenant."

"He confessed?" the Lieutenant raised his eyebrows and tapped the newspaper in front of him. "The guy's wife doesn't think he confessed, because she's pretty goddamn sure he didn't do it. The lawyer she hired doesn't think he confessed, because he says the guy has a goddamned ironclad alibi, and if we don't settle, we're about to get our fucking asses sued off. But you say—you say—he confessed."

The Lieutenant looked at the patrolman on the left. "Ryan, you were present in the interview room, is that correct?"

"Yessir."

"Did you hear a confession?"

"Well, Lieutenant, I heard him say something—"

"Jesus Christ!" the Lieutenant interrupted. "Learn to be a fucking witness. I asked you a yes or no question: Did you hear a confession?"

"No, Lieutenant."

The Lieutenant turned to the second patrolman. "McAndrews, did you hear a confession?"

"No, Lieutenant."

The Lieutenant let the words settle into the room, then turned toward the sofa. "Detective Stapleton, you interviewed this guy's wife?"

"Yes, Lieutenant."

"And she said what?"

Stapleton consulted the notebook balanced on his knee. "Aside from the usual statements that he was not the kind of person who could possibly have committed such a crime, she said that the only time they weren't together was when the old man took a shower or took a shit. Basically, they operate like Siamese twins. Always together."

"Conjoined twins, Stapleton, we call them conjoined twins nowadays," the Lieutenant said. "What is the age of the wife, Stapleton?"

Stapleton consulted his notes. "Seventy-seven, Lieutenant."

"How strong a witness would she be, what's her mental capacity?"

"On the shaky side, but pretty believable," Stapleton said. "She convinced me."

"Did this Walter whatever-his-name have a record, any priors?"

"Not even a parking ticket," Stapleton said.

"What a mess." The Lieutenant looked again at Garcia. "We've got ourselves a real lemon, here, Garcia, and it is of your making. Of your making."

On the sofa, Stapleton's leg gave Latimer's leg an imperceptible nudge, as if to say, this time there will be no lemonade.

The Lieutenant's gaze went back to Garcia. "What exactly did this asshole say in the way of a confession that only you heard, Garcia?"

"He said, 'I did it.'"

The Lieutenant took a few seconds to let that soak in.

"Patrolman Ryan, you said you heard something coming from the suspect, the witness, whatever the fuck he was."

"Yessir."

Garcia interrupted. "He said 'I did it.'"

"By any chance," the Lieutenant continued to address Ryan, "by any chance what you heard, did it sound like the words 'I did it'?"

"I couldn't tell, sir."

"But he said something."

"Yessir."

"And when he said whatever it was, did Detective Garcia respond?"

"Yessir."

"Very good, Ryan, very good. Yes or no, absolutely correct. And when Detective Garcia did respond, what did he say?"

"He said, 'that's a confession,' or something like that."

"He said 'that's a confession'" the Lieutenant said.

"That's right, Lieutenant."

"You heard this clearly, when Detective Garcia said 'that's a confession?'"

"Yes, Lieutenant."

"But you didn't hear the perpetrator, this goddamned sex killer, say 'I did it?'"

"No, Lieutenant."

"In view of Detective Garcia's response, Ryan, I think that's exactly what you did hear. I think you very clearly heard Walter Nick-whatever say 'I did it,' didn't you?"

"I guess I did, Sir."

"I guess I did? That's exactly what you heard, isn't it?"

"Yes, Lieutenant."

"And you, McAndrews," the Lieutenant turned to the second patrolman. "You heard exactly the same thing that your partner, Ryan, heard, because you were standing right there hearing exactly the same thing, isn't that correct?"

"That's correct, Lieutenant."

"So in the last moments before he died, this Walter whatever said, 'I did it.'" The Lieutenant turned his attention to the officers in front of the windows. "Sergeant Larkin, what do we call that, the statement the witness made?"

Larkin understood where the Lieutenant was going. "We call that a death-bed confession, Lieutenant."

"And what level of credence do the courts assign to a death-bed confession?"

"A very high level of credence, Lieutenant."

"You fuckin'-A-right. A very high level of credence."

The Lieutenant shuffled through a file on his desk and took out a photograph of the umbrella in the evidence bag, turning it toward Larkin. "And here we have a piece of evidence directly linked to the killer. A key piece of evidence. Would you say that's a key piece of evidence, Sergeant Larkin?"

Larkin cleared his throat. "A key piece of incontrovertible evidence, Lieutenant."

"You damn right. Incontrovertible evidence and a death-bed confession witnessed by three officers. I do believe that this crime has been solved. What do you believe, Sergeant Larkin?"

Sergeant Larkin cleared his throat. "The case appears to be open and shut, Lieutenant."

The Lieutenant looked again at Detective Garcia in front of him in the straight back chair, but this time he smiled. "I believe that Detective Garcia got a bee up his anal cavity and went off half-cocked and solved this case. What do you think, Sergeant Larkin?"

"It appears that Detective Garcia exercised a high degree of independent initiative, Lieutenant."

"A very high degree of initiative," the Lieutenant said. He looked around the room. Does anyone disagree with this conclusion? Are we in complete agreement, gentlemen? Have we taken a lemon and made lemonade?"

The Lieutenant allowed his gaze to sweep around the room, taking in the expressions of the men who looked impassively back at him.

"Yes, I think we have made some lemonade, gentlemen."

No one spoke, though Latimer's hand resting along the top of the couch did ease down and tap lightly on Stapleton's shoulder. When Stapleton looked over at Latimer, he saw Latimer's other hand, first two fingers and thumb rubbing together.

The Lieutenant turned to the Deputy Chief. "Chief, is there anything you'd like to add?"

The Deputy Chief, a portly man, stood up and crossed to Garcia, who got up from his chair. "Detective Garcia, congratulations on your aggressive police work. Everyone is proud of the way you cracked this case so quickly." He shook Garcia's hand. "I'm going to be putting in for a commendation on your behalf, Detective."

"Thank you," Garcia said, his voice weak.

"Ryan, McAndrews," the Deputy Chief said, turning to the patrolmen. "Fine work. Don't be surprised at a bump in grade coming your way next month."

Ryan and McAndrews thanked the Chief.

"Thanks, Chief. I think our work here is done, gentlemen," the Lieutenant said. "One word of caution. This case has its controversial elements, and it may give rise to a certain amount of departmental discussion. I want to hear no rumors or inklings around this place of any talk resulting from this meeting. Am I making myself clear on this?" The Lieutenant looked slowly around the room. "Then let's all get back on the job."

"God bless you boys for the work you're doing," the Deputy Chief added as they filed out of the office.

Harry tried to explain what had happened to a cab driver, who was some kind of Asian and who kept asking Harry for five dollars. Finally, Harry just gave him five dollars, because it didn't really matter anyway, and someone had to be the one that gave people what they asked for, and why shouldn't it be him? He told the driver he wanted to serve pussy, and the driver took him to a place that had peepshows. When Harry got out of the cab, he took the umbrella out from under his shirt, slipped it out of the sleeve, and opened it. The fabric had a silky sheen, he felt safe behind it.

The fat man behind the counter wore a greasy T-shirt. He

made Harry close the umbrella and charged him fifteen dollars to see the new pussy movie, which he said was the best one ever. He pointed Harry to a plywood alcove with a ratty stool in front of a television set and told him to wait a minute. The movie came up on the screen with no title and no credits, just a naked woman on her hands and knees with one man doing it to her from behind, another man doing it to her in the mouth and a third man playing with her swaying breasts. Then the man at her mouth withdrew, and she turned her head to look back at the man behind her and Harry saw that it was LaDonna and that the men were all doing it to her and doing it to her. Harry was sickened by it, but he couldn't stop watching. This was LaDonna, his LaDonna, the woman he loved, and the woman who loved him. "Oh, God, baby, I do love you so," she had said the last time Harry had served her with love. And now she was being served by these strangers, these fat old men with sagging bellies, who did everything to her while Harry sat and watched.

The movie ended and Harry walked out of the alcove, past the man behind the counter, who said, "Pretty good, huh?" Harry did not reply. Tears were streaming down his face. He had to walk three blocks down dark streets to find a cab. He just wanted to go home. The cabby made him close the umbrella so Harry closed it, put the cover on it, and put it back under his shirt, the handle up in his armpit.

LaDonna was in the living room when he let himself in. "Hi, baby," she called to him. "I was worried about you, come and sit down."

Harry listened to her complaints about her trip, and he tried very hard to be the same Harry that he used to be, but he knew she didn't really love him, certainly not the way he loved her, and he thought about the spinster sisters in North Park and how they, too, had stopped loving him, and he saw LaDonna, drunk, eyes bleary, sprawled across the big couch in front of the flatscreen, lipstick smeared on the rim of the glass on the coffee table, saw her in a way he hadn't seen her before, saw her as the piece of meat in the peepshow.

"Ca'mon," LaDonna said, pulling him close to her. "Do that voodoo to me that nobody does the way you do."

Harry took the umbrella out from beneath his shirt.

Christine and Teddy were alone in a corner of the network skybox high atop the rim of Qualcomm Stadium.

"You tried to talk him out of it?"

Christine nodded. "I showed him that article you printed out, the one that said the Boulder City guy did it. Harry told me the whole story. When he confessed, the way he confessed, he cried. I'm sure he killed the LaDonna person."

"You think he really did it?"

"I think he did. He knew details, he said he used an umbrella on her."

"How about remorse, did he show remorse?"

"He was really sad and guilty, and he wants to put himself to the test with God."

"You mean, God might float him down to earth."

"That's the test. If he's forgiven, if it's not his time, God will float him down."

"It's a trial by ordeal, it's how the criminal justice system worked a few hundred years ago. If you survived the trial, if you were able to hold a red hot iron bar in your hands, or you didn't drown when they threw you in the pond with a millstone tied to your neck, then you were innocent."

"That's how he sees it. One minute he's a lost little boy, the next minute it's like he's from some undiscovered land of nod somewhere."

Christine and Teddy watched the event from a row of chairs just behind a woman who, Christine thought, looked quite a bit like Imelda Marcos. She wondered why the network would have invited Imelda Marcos to their skybox.

Following the jugglers, the rock band, and the fireworks, Chariots of Fire surged through the sound system, and Harry, followed by spotlights, dressed in a white latex bodysuit with rhinestones that made him look like Elvis, slowly ascended the tower.

On a tiny platform at the top, Harry waited for the music to end. Then he stepped to the platform edge and an immense indrawn breath seemed to go through the crowd. Harry paused dramatically, arms outspread, just as the stage manager had instructed, then he slowly fell forward, almost, it seemed, as if he were falling in slow motion, and a child's lone voice shrieked, "He's flying!" and then his falling body was a blur in the air and it was over.

From the network's point of view, everything went off perfectly. In a minute a paramedic emerged from behind the curtain shielding the landing pad and gave the traditional Roman thumbs-down indicating Harry was dead.

As quickly as Death Leap was over, the crowd's excitement was gone, the indrawn breath at Harry's leap was exhaled, and now everyone's breathing returned to normal, and people turned to each other as if to say, Is that all? Nothing happens next?

As Christine sat in the skybox looking out over the rows of emptying seats, she felt a deep poignancy. She wondered for a moment what might have happened if Harry had never come up behind her at that party or if she had thrown him out.

But that was all so beside the point. Harry had undertaken his trial by ordeal and he had not floated down to earth. Harry's test was over and, she felt, so was hers.

She had been a willing participant, but was she a prime cause? No, it was Harry's decision, he had offered to try and fly and that had started it. She wasn't a judge, she wasn't a jury, but she was a lot more than a member of the audience. Then it came to her: She was the executive producer. She wondered if, in times gone by, when they had these ordeals, these trials by fire and water, the gladiators in the Roman Coliseum, was there someone who was the executive producer?

Had to have been.

Then her mood was gone as Klepner and five network people came over, all trying to hug her at once, and she was looking over their heads at Teddy, who leaned against a wall, watching her, not smiling, not frowning, just watching.

When he saw her eyes on him, he started making signals. You, me, out of here, get a drink. Then he blew her a kiss, and she smiled at him, it made her so happy.

She pursed her lips and sent him a kiss, and then she licked her upper lip, gave it plenty of tongue, and winked, and he smiled back and nodded. Yes, a drink and more than a drink. Tonight things would be different between them.

Two other network people, a man and a woman, both grinning, came up and began telling her how great the show was, how everyone in the country had been watching, what a huge number it was going to pull on the overnights. Then they shoved a little waif-like girl forward. "This is Harriet," the guy said, "that's what we're calling her. She wants to be next. It's gonna be Death Leap Two: the Girl. We want you to produce."

"Sorry," Christine said, disengaging herself , backing away. "That was it for me. I'm out of the business," and she walked away from them toward Teddy, who was holding out his hand to her.

About "Death Leap"

I thought I was writing a novel called *Pilgrims and Strangers*. I've still got a bunch of it on my hard drive. The novel started in San Diego, then moved to Las Vegas. Harry was a minor character in the novel, not LaDonna's killer, but rather her weak, frightened factotum who stood by as the real killer did his work. (The real killer was going to be the police lieutenant.)

It may be surprising to you (I don't know, maybe not) but I found Harry easy to write, he's such a simple soul. Maybe because he was fun to write, the way he's so irrational in such a logical way. His fascination with elbows came from Tallyrand's famous *bon mot* from 1846 or thereabouts: "Language was given to man to enable him to conceal his thoughts."

As for the beast that lurks beneath the ridges of the Nevada desert, am I the only one who has looked out the window on final approach to McCarran Airport and imagined the bony spines of some archaic animal beneath those hills?

That's how the subplot of an incomplete novel became a separate story of about twelve thousand words. Is that long enough to be a novella? Probably depends on who you ask (or prob'ly, as Harry would say).

The story-making process in this case was one of thinking you're doing one thing, writing a bunch of material separately: Harry's wanderings through Las Vegas; Christine and Russ, and then Christine and Teddy and Klepner; the cops at the crime scene and Detective Garcia, these were all written separately, at different times, and many of them were unrelated in my mind at the time they were written.

That might be why I never finished the novel. So then I sewed these separate bits together in the editing suite into a story quite different than the novel I had in mind when I started. Is this a viable way of working? Well, it produced this story, you can judge for yourself.

If you're working on something, and you get this urge to skip around and write this scene then that one out of sequence, seeming quite disconnected at the time, maybe your intuition is trying to tell you something, maybe along the lines of Oh, no, not another police procedural. What would happen if this nutcase runs into reality television…

"How do I make my character likable?"

My answer is always the same: Forget likable, make your character interesting.

That's what I was doing with Harry and certainly with Christine when I was writing. Or what I thought I was doing. What I was really doing with Christine was making her into someone the reader would envy. Going back and reading about character in Dwight Swain's *Techniques of the Selling Writer* (Chapter 7), he cites *envy* as being a primary characteristic of a good protagonist. If you were a woman at cocktail party and someone dissed you, wouldn't you sort of like to be able to handle it the way Christine handled it? Turn on the s.o.b. and threaten to put him on him ass? (That's the way I wish the women would have reacted when Harvey Weinstein came out of the bathroom naked, picked up the nearest heavy glass ashtray and put him on his butt. Maybe that would have slowed him down.)

Once Christine shifts gears and has the idea for the show, she reverts to 10-year-old playground logic:

"Hey," she said, "he likes me better than he likes you. Why can't you just accept it?"

Then, a moment later:

"He's mine. I saw him first and he's mine."

Playground logic isn't deep and philosophical, there's no nuance. Don't you wish sometimes you could say, "I saw it first," and grab whatever it might be? Instead we're all civilized and we say, "After you, my dear Alphonse" and grit our teeth.

Later in the story, with a few quick masterstrokes of logic, she persuades Teddy to come to work for her. Then she extorts Klepner out of ten million dollars. Of course we like her, she's everything we wish we could be, and envy is the source of that wish.

I've always enjoyed Las Vegas. When my mother, an RN, MPH, was working for Kaiser Permanente in the San Fernando Valley, a couple times of year she would invite me and sometimes others to accompany her to Las Vegas. She was an avid bridge player, traveled to tournaments, accumulated master points and so on. She liked to play blackjack, and on these jaunts would bring along a supply of dexies. Every four hours she would say, "It's time for your pill." We would stay up all night at the blackjack tables and drink complimentary screwdrivers as the sun came up.

The police force in Las Vegas has always struck me as being

highly efficient and incorruptible; I hope no one imagines my fictional version is anything other than imaginary, the bizarro attempt at an amusing tale.

If you enjoyed the book, please take a couple minutes to leave a review.

Acknowledgments

Many of the books and stories I've learned from are cited in the text, and there are others that deserve special mention.

My oldest sister, Ann Spencer Hume, the English teacher, exhibited great patience and perseverance over the years in reading my stories, and tried valiantly, usually in vain, to correct my punctuation.

My thanks to the gang of colleagues at several writing sites over the years, the most recent being Scribophile, who put up with me for the past decade or so, with whom I shared many laughs, and from whom I learned a great deal.

Thanks to my grandchildren, Spencer and Avery, who, quite unknowingly, were responsible for so many things, like The Forgetful Pirates, an afternoon at the Ostrich Rectangle, and Spencer's illustrated handmade Book of Weirdos, long lost but never forgotten. The memories have been an always-there touch-stone of carefree happiness I treasure. (Is this is my own Book of Weirdos?) It's been hard work, this refusal to grow up, but thanks to my wife, Pamela, for putting up with me, my children, Wyatt and Emily, and the grandchildren, I think I've managed it reasonably well.

Thanks to CHRISTOPHER WYLIE and his exceptionally important book, *Mindfu***k: Cambridge Analytica and the Plot to Break America*, for the epigram that sums up what goes on in writers' heads.

I've encountered a great deal of generosity in the preparation of this book, and owe dollops of gratitude to:

BARRY EISLER for permission to reprint his essay on resonance in titles;

CLIFF ROBISON for permission to quote from his novel *Bell, Book and Bullets*, published by Rock and Fire Press, copyright 2016, and to quote his postings about creating language;

FRANK LADD for the use of his story *Falls Road*, published by Akashic Books, copyright 2017;

EMMA DARWIN, PhD, to quote from her blog *This Itch of Writing*;

SOUTHERN ILLINOIS UNIVERSITY PRESS to quote from *Backwards & Forwards, a Technical Manual for Reading Plays* by David Ball, copyright 1983;

SHIRLEY GOLDEN for permission to reprint her story *Double Trouble*;

MICHAEL TEDIN for his blog, Worldbuilding 102;

UNIVERSITY OF OKLAHOMA PRESS for permission to excerpt from *Techniques of the Selling Writer* by Dwight V. Swain, copyright 1973.

Prizes and Awards

First Place for Fiction, San Diego Writers/Editors Guild 1982
First Place for Non-Fiction, San Diego Writers/Editors
Guild 1983
First Prize, Ursus Press Short Story Competition 1985
First Place for Fiction, San Diego Writers/Editors Guild 1986
First Place for Essay, San Diego Writers/Editors Guild 1986
First Place for Fiction, San Diego Writers/Editors Guild 1987
ITVA — International Television Association Award of Excellence 1989
Shooting Star Award, American Corporate Video Awards, 1990
12th Annual Pacific Southwest Regional Telly Award, 1991

About the Author

After college I had about 15 different jobs. I kicked around from New York to Seattle to Los Angeles to Johnston Island in the Central Pacific, from Los Altos and Palo Alto to Saigon to Yakima to San Diego. At one point Robert Goulet recorded one of my 60 second spots with exactly the intonation I heard when I wrote it. My friend Ted Klein, who knew *everyone*, set me up with a phone call to try to get Isaac Asimov to write an article for the Syntex annual report, but Asimov wouldn't travel on airplanes and a train trip across the country to California wasn't in the cards. It was an interesting time to be young: I saw the Maharishi Mahesh Yogi speak in Hollywood; watched Leonard Bernstein conduct Bartók's *Symphony for Orchestra* at Carnegie Hall, and watched Irving "The Deacon" Crane run 109 balls at straight pool in Las Vegas. But that's all in the long ago past. Now I'm retired, live in San Diego with my wife, Pamela. We have two children and two grandchildren.

Made in United States
North Haven, CT
15 December 2022

28499468R00166